Book H

LANGUAGE Power

1120 Birchmount Road
Toronto, Ontario M1K 5G4
1-800-668-0671
www.nelson.com

Editorial Team: Chelsea Donaldson, Evelyn Maksimovich
Cover Adaptation: Christine Dandurand

ISBN-13: **978-0-7715-1040-3**
ISBN-10: **0-7715-1040-3**

7 8 9 WC 08 07 06

Written, printed, and bound in Canada

Table of Contents

Unit 1 Vocabulary

Unit 2 Sentences

Unit 3 Grammar and Usage

Unit 4 Capitalization and Punctuation

Unit 5 Composition

Unit 6 Study Skills

Final Review

Lesson 1 Word Origins: Greek Roots

- Many technical terms used in science and technology are formed by combining common Greek words.

  EXAMPLE: The term biology is a combination of bios, a Greek word meaning "life," and logos, a Greek word meaning "the study of."

Word	Meaning	Word	Meaning
bio	life	-logy, -ology	science of, study of
dynamo, dynamic	power, force	-graphy	writing, recording
eco	habitat, environment	-metry, metric	measurement of
ergon	work	-osis	art, process, state, condition
geo	earth	-otic, -otics	pertaining to, of
hydro	water		
photo	light		
tele	far, distant		
thermo	heat		
zoo	animal		

For each scientific and technical term below, choose the correct definition from the list at the right side of the page and write the corresponding letter in the space provided. Then use each word in a sentence. Write the sentences in your notebook.

1. biometric _____
2. biology _____
3. hydrothermal _____
4. thermodynamic _____
5. zoology _____
6. ecosystem _____
7. geothermal _____
8. photometry _____
9. biotic _____
10. hydrology _____

(a) the interaction of living things with one another and with their habitat

(b) the study of animals

(c) having to do with hot water

(d) the calculation or measurement of the duration of human life

(e) measurement of the intensity of light

(f) having to do with heat produced in the earth

(g) using the force derived from heat

(h) pertaining to life

(i) the study of bodies of water

(j) the study of living things

Lesson 2

Word Origins: Latin Roots

- Many English words have Latin roots.
  EXAMPLE: Video comes from the Latin root word videre, meaning "see."

A. For each Latin root below, provide another example of an English word. Check your words in a dictionary that gives word origins.

	Latin Root	English Forms	Examples	
1.	dicere (say)	dic, dict	contradict, dictate,	diction
2.	videre (see)	vid, vis	video, visible,	visual
3.	mittere (send)	mit, miss	submit, mission,	missing
4.	audire (hear)	audio, aud	audio, audible,	auditorium
5.	scribere (write)	scrib, script	describe, script,	discriptive
6.	specere (look)	spec, spect	aspect, spectacle,	spectacular
7.	radius (ray)	radio, rad	radio, radius,	radical
8.	labor (work)	labor, labour	elaborate, laboratory,	elaborate
9.	ducere (bring)	duct, duce, duit	conduct, reduce	suduce
10.	putare (think, calculate)	put	dispute, putative	putter

B. Replace the underlined phrase with a word that contains the Latin root shown in parentheses.

1. I will look closely at inspect your uniforms in the morning. (specere)
2. The people listening to the show audience clapped wildly when the concert was over. (audire)
3. The device that emits heat radiater in my car is leaking again. (radius)
4. The two scientists worked together elaborated on this research. (labor)
5. It appears that isvisisable you prefer him to me. (videre)
6. No one can say what will happen in predict. the future. (dicere)
7. The self-propelled rocket miss will hit the target at 0900 hours. (mittere)
8. The doctor gave me a written order perscription for antibiotics. (scribere)
9. Josh used a machine for calculating computar to create the database. (putare)
10. You are expected to bring forth produce two major essays this term. (ducere)

Lesson 3

Prefixes

- A **prefix** added to the **beginning of a base word** changes the meaning of the word.

  EXAMPLE: re- meaning "again" + the base word view = review, meaning "view again"

EXAMPLES:

Prefix	Meaning
con-, com-	together
de-	do the opposite of, remove
dis-	opposite of, lack of
in-, il-, im- ir- un-	not
mis-	bad, badly, wrong, wrongly
post-	after
pre-	before
re-	again, back
sub-	below

A. Add the prefix un-, in-, im-, il-, or ir- to the word in parentheses. Write the new word in the sentence. Use a dictionary if necessary.

1. It is ______________ (responsible) to throw snowballs at cars.
2. Your alien abduction story sounds very ______________ (probable).
3. Too much ______________ (activity) is unhealthy.
4. An ______________ (logical) argument will not convince your opponents.
5. Cut the cake into two ______________ (equal) pieces and give me the bigger one.
6. I have an ______________ (rational) fear of spiders.
7. Early settlers to Canada endured ______________ (imaginable) hardships.
8. Your handwriting is ______________ (legible).
9. You are doing all of us an ______________ (justice) by your ______________ (just) treatment of those workers.
10. The warranty is void because of ______________ (proper) use.

B. The following words contain prefixes. Write the meaning of each word in your notebook, and then write the word in a sentence.

1. disapproval
2. revisit
3. repay
4. preregister
5. substandard
6. postwar
7. misgovern
8. decentralize
9. conjoin
10. irreplaceable

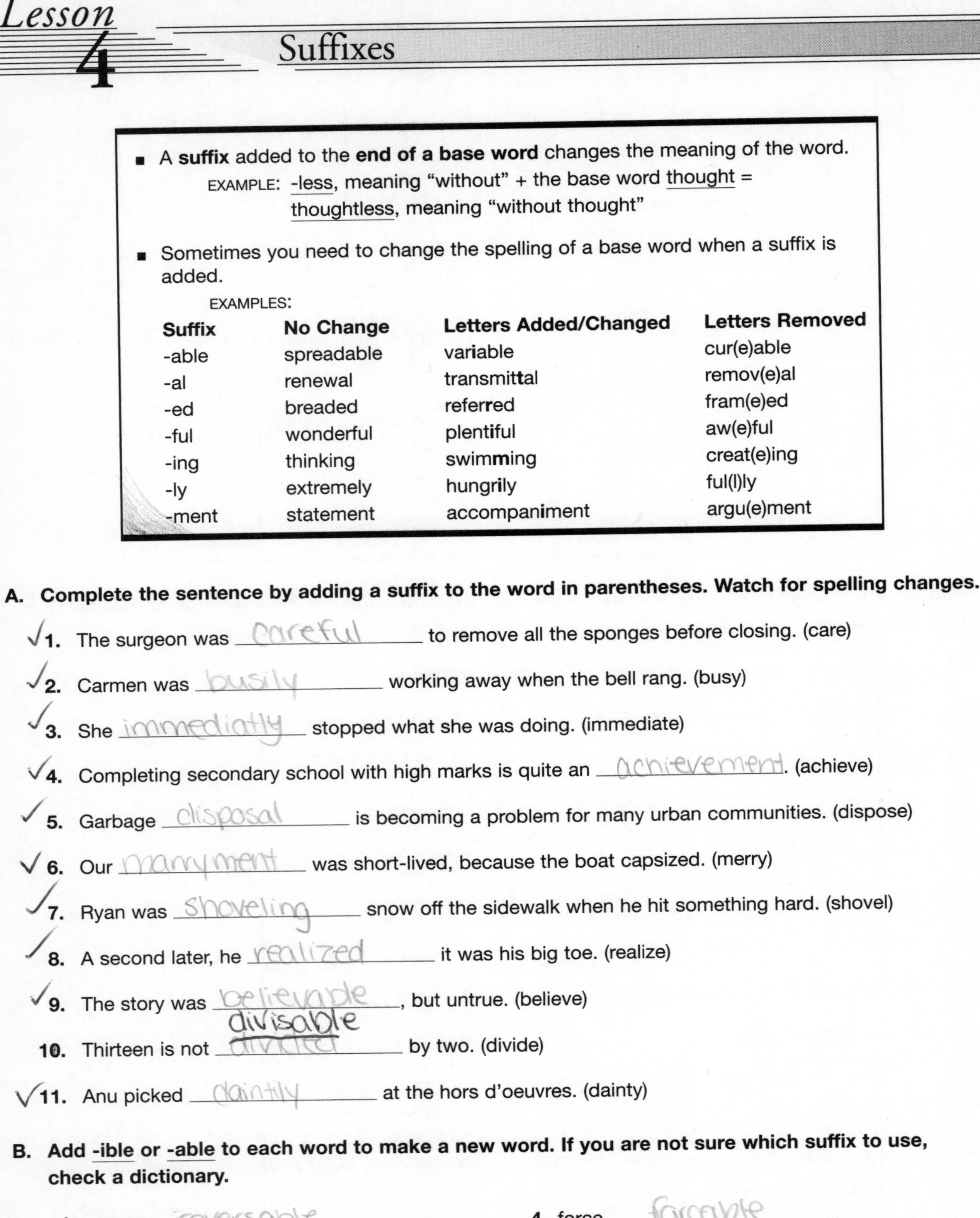

Lesson 4 Suffixes

- A **suffix** added to the **end of a base word** changes the meaning of the word.

  EXAMPLE: -less, meaning "without" + the base word thought = thoughtless, meaning "without thought"

- Sometimes you need to change the spelling of a base word when a suffix is added.

  EXAMPLES:

Suffix	No Change	Letters Added/Changed	Letters Removed
-able	spreadable	variable	cur(e)able
-al	renewal	transmittal	remov(e)al
-ed	breaded	referred	fram(e)ed
-ful	wonderful	plentiful	aw(e)ful
-ing	thinking	swimming	creat(e)ing
-ly	extremely	hungrily	ful(l)ly
-ment	statement	accompaniment	argu(e)ment

A. Complete the sentence by adding a suffix to the word in parentheses. Watch for spelling changes.

✓ 1. The surgeon was careful to remove all the sponges before closing. (care)

✓ 2. Carmen was busily working away when the bell rang. (busy)

✓ 3. She immediatly stopped what she was doing. (immediate)

✓ 4. Completing secondary school with high marks is quite an achievement. (achieve)

✓ 5. Garbage disposal is becoming a problem for many urban communities. (dispose)

✓ 6. Our marryment was short-lived, because the boat capsized. (merry)

✓ 7. Ryan was shoveling snow off the sidewalk when he hit something hard. (shovel)

✓ 8. A second later, he realized it was his big toe. (realize)

✓ 9. The story was believable, but untrue. (believe)

10. Thirteen is not ~~divided~~ divisable by two. (divide)

✓ 11. Anu picked daintily at the hors d'oeuvres. (dainty)

B. Add -ible or -able to each word to make a new word. If you are not sure which suffix to use, check a dictionary.

1. reverse reversable
2. notice noticeable
3. collapse collapsible
4. force forcable
5. desire desirable
6. receive receivable.

Homophones

- **Homophones** are words that have the same sound but different spellings and meanings.

  EXAMPLE: We are allowed to stay out until midnight.
  He read the statement aloud so everyone could hear.

Circle the correct homophone in each sentence that follows. Then write a sentence using the other homophone(s).

1. In the (passed, past) this place was used as a hospital.

   She passed the ball to me.

2. The rebels engaged in (gorilla, guerrilla) warfare against the government troops.

   The gorilla ate the mango.

3. That scarf would (complement, compliment) my outfit perfectly.

   Thanks for the compliment on my outfit.

4. "I'm (threw, through) with you!" cried Ashley.

   She threw a pan at me.

5. It will probably take a few weeks for your foot to (heal, heel).

   My dog wounded it heel.

6. I could hear the bells (pealing, peeling) all the way across the meadow.

   I was pealing a banana when I was hit by a frisbee.

7. My actions were based on a sound (principal, principle).

   The principal suspended me.

8. The warrior sallied (forth, fourth) on her trusty steed to fight evil.

   The fourth one was ugly.

9. In my essay about the Great Depression, I (cite, site) a book by Pierre Berton.

   What a Site!

10. While swimming, beavers use (their, there, they're) broad tails as rudders.

    a) Over there is a hippo.

    b) They're insane.

11. Tenzing Norgay and Sir Edmund Hillary completed their (ascent, assent) of Mount Everest in 1953.

12. The rear (brake, break) on my bicycle needs to be adjusted.

Lesson 6 Idioms

- An **idiom** is an expression that has a meaning different from the usual meaning of the individual words within it.

  EXAMPLE: Let's hit the road means "Let's get going," not "Let's strike the ground."

A. Read each sentence. Then write the letter of the corresponding idiom for the underlined word or words.

(a) come up with	(e) in the red	(i) across the board
(b) come down with	(f) a heart of stone	(j) under the weather
(c) come through	(g) feet of clay	
(d) in the pink	(h) through the grapevine	

1. My boss seemed perfect at first, but she turned out to have human failings like everybody else. g
2. Analysts say prices will increase in all areas this year. i
3. If you don't get a flu shot, you may contract a nasty bug. b
4. We all knew that you would be successful in the end. c
5. It's obvious that Kayla is feeling good. d
6. We need to provide the answer by Monday! a
7. I heard from other people that you are leaving. h
8. That company is losing money. e
9. You would have to have no pity not to be moved by the faces of those children. f
10. I have been feeling sick for a few days now. j

B. Write the meaning of the following idioms.

1. Stanley seems out of sorts today. not normal/not himself.
2. That's because he and Stuart locked horns yesterday. disagreed
3. Stu really gave him a piece of his mind. told him off
4. He said he was fed up with Stan not coming to rehearsals. had enough
5. Then he asked Stanley if he would like to bow out of the play. quit
6. Stanley told Stuart to lighten up. forget about it
7. But he did promise to quit horsing around. being silly
8. Stuart and Stanley go back a long way. how we've known eachother for a while
9. I'm sure they'll patch things up soon. make up
10. Let's hope they get their act together before opening night! figure things out

Lesson 7

Colloquialisms and Slang

- A **colloquialism** is a word or expression that is used in speech or informal writing, but is not appropriate in more formal written work.

  EXAMPLE: The colloquial expression in the sentence, "Wilfrid Laurier was crazy about his dogs," would be acceptable in conversation or written dialogue, but would not be acceptable in a history paper or other formal writing.

- **Slang** is language that is relatively new and often used by a specific group of people to set themselves apart from others. Slang is not appropriate in formal writing, and should be used sparingly, even in informal writing.

  EXAMPLE: Computer users sometimes refer to postal services by the slang term snail mail.

- In the dictionary, colloquialisms are often labelled "informal," while slang, if it does not pass quickly out of use, is usually labelled "slang." Both colloquialisms and slang are listed under the entry for the most important word in the expression.

  EXAMPLE: The expression over the hill is listed under "hill" in the dictionary.

A. Replace each of the underlined expressions with a more formal word or expression.

1. I can't believe my boss gave me the boot! fired me.
2. I think I'm getting the hang of hang-gliding. understanding
3. So you lost! Don't dump on me! vent
4. I can't go to the concert because I haven't got any dough. money
5. The first car I bought was a real lemon. poor quality
6. You know how much it bugs me when you talk like that. annoys
7. Well, you don't have to blow up at me! get mad.
8. *Romeo and Juliet* is a real tearjerker! emotional play
9. I got this cut when I wiped out on my bike. Crashed
10. The rain showed no signs of letting up. lighting up.

B. Identify five slang expressions that you use when speaking with your friends, but that you would not use in formal writing. Write the meaning of each expression.

1. Whats up? What are you doing.
2. Beauts McGee. That would be beautiful.
3. Golden perfect.
4.
5.

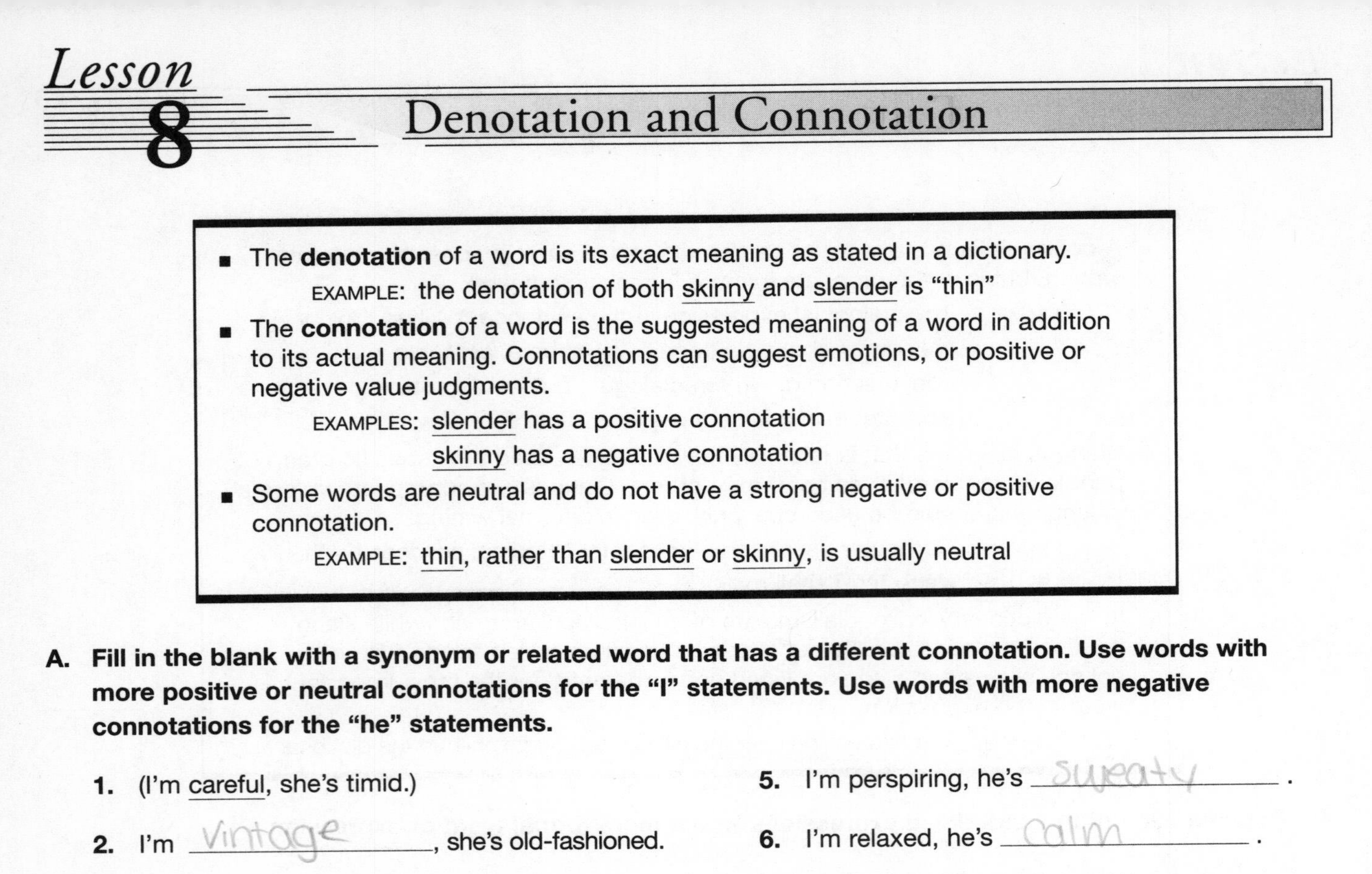

Lesson 8 Denotation and Connotation

- The **denotation** of a word is its exact meaning as stated in a dictionary.
  EXAMPLE: the denotation of both skinny and slender is "thin"
- The **connotation** of a word is the suggested meaning of a word in addition to its actual meaning. Connotations can suggest emotions, or positive or negative value judgments.
  EXAMPLES: slender has a positive connotation
  skinny has a negative connotation
- Some words are neutral and do not have a strong negative or positive connotation.
  EXAMPLE: thin, rather than slender or skinny, is usually neutral

A. Fill in the blank with a synonym or related word that has a different connotation. Use words with more positive or neutral connotations for the "I" statements. Use words with more negative connotations for the "he" statements.

1. (I'm careful, she's timid.)
2. I'm vintage, she's old-fashioned.
3. I'm adventerous, she's reckless.
4. I'm selfabsorbed, she's naive.
5. I'm perspiring, he's sweaty.
6. I'm relaxed, he's calm.
7. I'm curious, he's nosey.
8. I save, he spends his money.

B. Rewrite the following paragraph. Replace the underlined words with others that have a more positive or neutral connotation.

I love camping. I love to listen to the savage beasts as they barge into my campsite to devour my leftovers. The sound of a radio blaring, or of giddy campers searching for the outhouse at two in the morning are true wilderness experiences. In the tent, the shrill whine of a mosquito looking for blood reminds me of the life-and-death struggles taking place nightly in the murky woods outside. I especially enjoy huddling around the campfire, as the flames dance higher and the heat scorches my face. And what could be better than eating lumps of charred marshmallow from the end of a stick? Oh, yes, I do love camping.

I love Camping. I love to listen to the birds as they fly around my cabin to snack on my leftovers. The sound of the radio playing or of frightened campers searching for the out house at two in the morning are true wilderness expiriances. In the tent, the faint whine of a mosquito looking for blood reminds me of the life and death struggles taking place nightly in the dense woods out side. I especially enjoy standing around the campfire .... warms.... pieces of melted...

Lesson 9

Euphemisms

- A **euphemism** is a mild or indirect way to express something harsh or unpleasant.

  EXAMPLE: pass away is a euphemism for die

A. Replace the underlined word with a euphemistic word or phrase.

1. I need to go to the toilet. washroom/bathroom
2. He was buried in Memory Gardens. put
3. Old people get a 10-percent discount. Ceniors
4. I am going to have my dog killed at the vet. put down
5. If you are drunk, you should never drive a car. imparred

B. Underline the euphemisms in the following sentences. Write the word or phrase that has been replaced on the line.

1. I was downsized from my job last year. downsized
2. I am currently between jobs. between
3. I bought a previously enjoyed stereo through the classifieds. previously enjoyed
4. That house is being advertised as a fixer-upper. fixerupper.

C. Write sentences using two more euphemisms for each of the following words.

1. dead

   a) non excistant

   b) passed away

2. poor

   a) notwealthy

   b) broke.

3. second-hand

   a) previously owned

   b) passed on

4. old

   a) Vintage

   b) ancient.

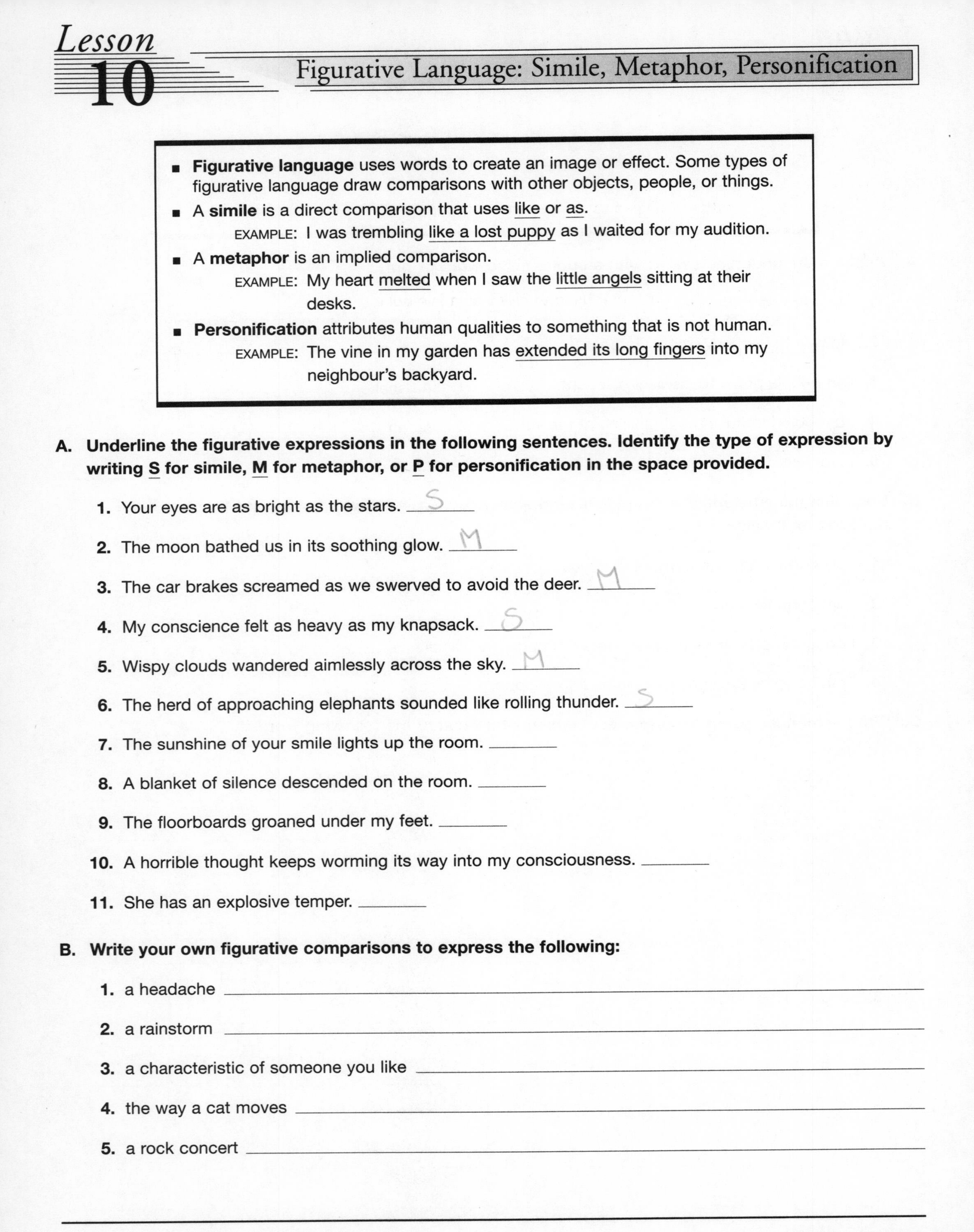

Lesson 10

Figurative Language: Simile, Metaphor, Personification

- **Figurative language** uses words to create an image or effect. Some types of figurative language draw comparisons with other objects, people, or things.
- A **simile** is a direct comparison that uses like or as.
  EXAMPLE: I was trembling like a lost puppy as I waited for my audition.
- A **metaphor** is an implied comparison.
  EXAMPLE: My heart melted when I saw the little angels sitting at their desks.
- **Personification** attributes human qualities to something that is not human.
  EXAMPLE: The vine in my garden has extended its long fingers into my neighbour's backyard.

A. Underline the figurative expressions in the following sentences. Identify the type of expression by writing S for simile, M for metaphor, or P for personification in the space provided.

1. Your eyes are as bright as the stars. S
2. The moon bathed us in its soothing glow. M
3. The car brakes screamed as we swerved to avoid the deer. M
4. My conscience felt as heavy as my knapsack. S
5. Wispy clouds wandered aimlessly across the sky. M
6. The herd of approaching elephants sounded like rolling thunder. S
7. The sunshine of your smile lights up the room. ______
8. A blanket of silence descended on the room. ______
9. The floorboards groaned under my feet. ______
10. A horrible thought keeps worming its way into my consciousness. ______
11. She has an explosive temper. ______

B. Write your own figurative comparisons to express the following:

1. a headache ______
2. a rainstorm ______
3. a characteristic of someone you like ______
4. the way a cat moves ______
5. a rock concert ______

Lesson 11 Figurative Language: Symbols

- A **symbol** is an object that is used to represent something more than itself.
  EXAMPLE: at a wedding, the ring symbolizes eternity, wholeness, and continuity, because it has no beginning and no ending

When writers use symbols, they often use them in a specific way that fits the context of the story or poem. For example, a tree is a universal symbol of knowledge, truth, life, and so on. However, in a particular work, an author might use a tree that a character used to climb as a symbol of childhood.

A. Identify the quality that each of the following animals symbolizes.

1. lion ______(courage)______
2. lamb ____________
3. dog ____________
4. snake ____________
5. ant ____________
6. bird ____________

B. Write the colour that might symbolize each of the following qualities or ideas.

1. purity ____________
2. anger ____________
3. death ____________
4. cowardice ____________
5. peacefulness ____________
6. royalty ____________

C. Explain what qualities of fire make it an appropriate symbol for each of the following. Write a sentence that uses that quality of fire as a symbol.

1. change or transformation ____________

____

____

2. passion ____________

____

____

3. inspiration, creativity ____________

____

____

4. comfort, contentment ____________

____

____

Review

A. Underline the English forms of the Greek or Latin root word in each of the following. Then write two other words that you have already learned that have the same root.

1. suspect ______________________
2. dynamite ______________________
3. dictionary ______________________
4. hydrated ______________________
5. commit ______________________
6. inaudible ______________________
7. radial ______________________

B. Choose an appropriate prefix from the box for each of the underlined words, and then write the word in the first space provided. Use each prefix only once. Then add the suffix to the new word.

de-	dis-	post-	sub-	un-

1. not happy ____________ + -ly = ____________
2. below the conscious level ____________ + -ly = ____________
3. lack of respect ____________ + -ful = ____________
4. to date after the current date ____________ + -ed = ____________
5. to remove a bone or bones ____________ + -ing = ____________

C. Choose from the homophones in parentheses to complete each sentence correctly. Use a dictionary, if necessary.

1. (formally, formerly) The woman who was ____________ known as Lucinda has started proceedings to ____________ change her name to Lulu.
2. (elicit, illicit) The police could not ____________ a response when they asked the suspect where he got the ____________ drugs.
3. (coarse, course) Of ____________, I prefer ____________ salt on my pretzels.
4. (all together, altogether) If we travel ____________ to Ottawa in the same car, it will be ____________ too crowded.
5. (their, there, they're) If ____________ isn't enough room for ____________ suitcases, ____________ going to ask for a bigger car.

D. Underline the idiom in each sentence. Using a dictionary, write I for informal (colloquial), or S for slang.

1. I had a falling-out with my friend Hugh. __________
2. If I didn't already have a girlfriend, I could really fall for Jassanthy! __________
3. After the fire, Yuri invited Steven to stay with him until he was back on his feet. __________
4. It's easy to run up a big bill on a credit card, isn't it? __________
5. When Delma visited, we sat and chewed the fat for hours! __________

E. Suggest a word or expression with a more positive or neutral connotation to replace the underlined word(s) in each sentence.

1. That pesky reporter is at the door again. ____________________
2. Tell him I have no more gossip for him today. ____________________
3. Did you rat to the police about the pollution at the factory? ____________________
4. I told them that chemicals were spewing out into the river. ____________________
5. Now the newspapers are hounding me for more information. ____________________

F. Match the euphemism on the left with the corresponding job on the right.

1. sanitary engineer	__________	(a) secretary
2. domestic engineer	__________	(b) painter
3. personal assistant	__________	(c) garbage collector
4. resurfacing technician	__________	(d) homemaker

G. Label each of the following either S for simile, M for metaphor, or P for personification.

1. His life was an open book. __________
2. "My love is like a red, red rose...." (Robert Burns) __________
3. The dry leaves gathered in groups, chattering gaily. __________
4. "I wandered lonely as a cloud...." (William Wordsworth) __________
5. The train slithered up the mountain, letting out a hiss as it reached the top. __________
6. The blank page stared up at me, daring me to sit down and write something. __________
7. A lone siren pierced the stillness of the night. __________
8. The car engine grumbled and protested all the way to the top of the hill. __________

Using What You've Learned

A. Replace the underlined phrase with a word that contains the Greek or Latin root in parentheses.

1. When the firefighters arrived, they attached the hose to the pipe holding water. (hydro) ____________

2. The producers listened to the performance of over 20 singers before choosing me for the part. (audire) ____________

3. The study of the environment is a scientific field that will become more important in the future. (eco) ____________

4. From my point of view things are looking good. (specere) ____________

5. I really believe that our leader is a person who sees more clearly than the rest of us. (videre) ____________

B. Add one of the following prefixes or suffixes to each base word to make a new word.

Prefixes: mis-, con-, re-, un-, dis-	**Suffixes:** -ment, -ful, -less, -ed, -able

1. base ____________
2. play ____________
3. take ____________
4. firm ____________
5. move ____________
6. shoe ____________
7. skill ____________
8. tie ____________
9. appoint ____________
10. cure ____________

C. Underline the misused homophone in each of the following sentences. Then write the correct homophone.

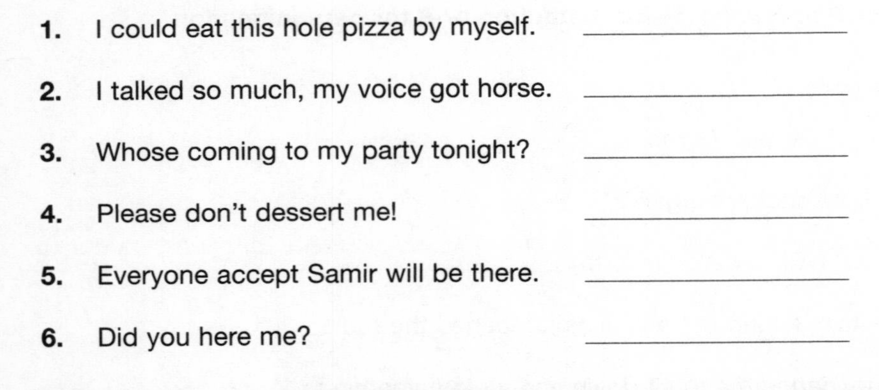

1. I could eat this hole pizza by myself. ____________
2. I talked so much, my voice got horse. ____________
3. Whose coming to my party tonight? ____________
4. Please don't dessert me! ____________
5. Everyone accept Samir will be there. ____________
6. Did you here me? ____________

D. Write a sentence using each of the following idioms. Use a dictionary, if necessary.

1. (to be beside oneself) ____________________________________

2. (give someone the cold shoulder) ______________________________

____

3. (in a nutshell) ______________________________

____

4. (on the mend) ______________________________

____

5. (keep in touch) ______________________________

____

E. Replace the words in parentheses with words or expressions that have an appropriate connotation.

1. When my aunt won the lottery, she (yelled) ______________ for joy.
2. As his bare feet touched the hot sand, he (yelled) ______________ in pain.
3. Her room was a mess; clothes were (placed) ______________ all over the floor.
4. Her room was immaculate; clothes were (placed) ______________ in neat rows on the shelves.
5. John (walked) ______________ into the classroom 15 minutes late, as usual, without his books, and with a sly grin on his face.
6. The teacher (walked) ______________ up to John's desk and demanded to know why he was late.

F. Create an original simile to complete each of the following:

1. soft as ______________________________
2. sad as ______________________________
3. mad as ______________________________
4. pretty as ______________________________
5. quiet as ______________________________

G. Write a description of weather conditions that could be used to symbolize the following moods or states of mind.

1. happiness, joy (The sun was shining brightly, with not a cloud in the sky.)
2. worry, uneasiness ______________________________
3. anger, fear ______________________________
4. sorrow, depression ______________________________
5. excitement ______________________________

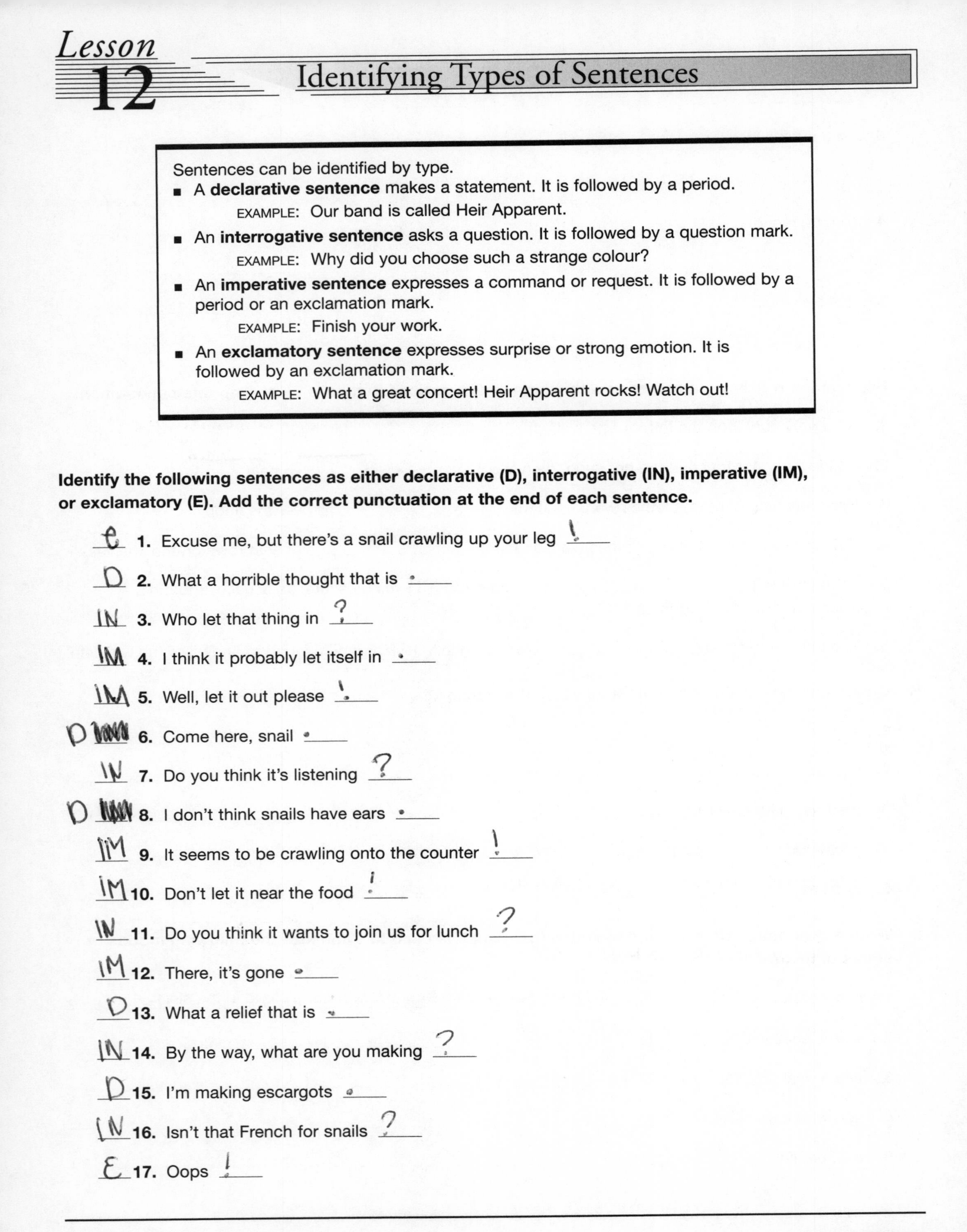

Lesson 12 Identifying Types of Sentences

Sentences can be identified by type.

- A **declarative sentence** makes a statement. It is followed by a period.
  EXAMPLE: Our band is called Heir Apparent.
- An **interrogative sentence** asks a question. It is followed by a question mark.
  EXAMPLE: Why did you choose such a strange colour?
- An **imperative sentence** expresses a command or request. It is followed by a period or an exclamation mark.
  EXAMPLE: Finish your work.
- An **exclamatory sentence** expresses surprise or strong emotion. It is followed by an exclamation mark.
  EXAMPLE: What a great concert! Heir Apparent rocks! Watch out!

Identify the following sentences as either declarative (D), interrogative (IN), imperative (IM), or exclamatory (E). Add the correct punctuation at the end of each sentence.

E **1.** Excuse me, but there's a snail crawling up your leg !

D **2.** What a horrible thought that is .

IN **3.** Who let that thing in ?

IM **4.** I think it probably let itself in .

IM **5.** Well, let it out please !

D **6.** Come here, snail .

IN **7.** Do you think it's listening ?

D **8.** I don't think snails have ears .

IM **9.** It seems to be crawling onto the counter !

IM **10.** Don't let it near the food !

IN **11.** Do you think it wants to join us for lunch ?

IM **12.** There, it's gone .

D **13.** What a relief that is .

IN **14.** By the way, what are you making ?

D **15.** I'm making escargots .

IN **16.** Isn't that French for snails ?

E **17.** Oops !

Lesson 13 Natural Order and Inverted Order Sentences

- When the subject of a sentence comes before the verb, the sentence is in **natural order**.

  EXAMPLES: The soldier ran over the hill.
  Rosa does love pizza.
  The keys are here.

- When the verb or part of the verb comes before the subject, the sentence is in **inverted order**. Most questions are in inverted order. So are sentences that begin with here is, here are, there is, or there are. Writers sometimes use inverted order to create an effect or to change the emphasis in a sentence.

  EXAMPLES: Over the hill ran the soldier.
  Does Rosa love pizza?
  Here are the keys.

A. Rewrite each sentence in natural order. Change questions to statements, if necessary.

1. Around that corner is a music shop. ______________________
2. Never have I seen so many guitars. ______________________
3. Does he want to go home already? ______________________
4. Here is my knapsack. ______________________
5. Off came their hats! ______________________
6. There, hiding under a rock, was the key. ______________________
7. Did your dirt bike get stuck in the mud? ______________________

B. Rewrite each sentence in inverted order. Underline the subject and circle the verb in each new sentence.

1. My bean plant is here. ______________________
2. The balloon in the little girl's hand went BANG. ______________________
3. Elijah sat in the first row, grinning from ear to ear. ______________________
4. "Oh, no," Jasper whispered. ______________________
5. Suddenly, Marnie was there, hugging me! ______________________
6. You keep your glasses where? ______________________
7. The foundering ship sank beneath the waves. ______________________

C. Write two inverted-order sentences of your own.

1. ______________________
2. ______________________

Subjects and Predicates

- Every sentence has two main parts, a **complete subject** and a **complete predicate**.
- The **complete subject** includes all the words that tell who or what the sentence is about, including a noun or pronoun.

  EXAMPLES: The corner store rents videos.
  This plastic moose wallet reminds me of home.
- The **complete predicate** includes all the words that state the action or condition of the subject, including a verb.

  EXAMPLES: The corner store rents videos.
  This plastic moose wallet reminds me of home.

A. Draw a vertical line between the complete subject and the complete predicate in each sentence.

1. Shakespeare wrote many plays.
2. My dog likes to eat cereal for breakfast.
3. Cotton-candy-flavoured potato chips never really caught on.
4. The Rocky Mountains rose up suddenly before us.
5. The girl over there with the great batting arm is Marissa.
6. Several of us near the front of the roller coaster lost our lunch.
7. I thought long and hard about your kind offer before refusing it.
8. The books on the table need to be put away.
9. Your cousin Inigo would like to be a cartoonist.
10. Her big, blue, saucer-shaped eyes gazed back at me.

B. Add words to the subject and/or the predicate to expand the sentences that follow. Then draw a vertical line between the complete subject and the complete predicate in each sentence.

1. The thunder roared. The thunder | roared across the sky.
2. My stomach growled. My stomache | growled very loudly during class.
3. The car sped. The car | sped up to make the light.
4. Her hair blew. Her hair | blew in the wind
5. My plan failed. My plan | to attend the dance failed.

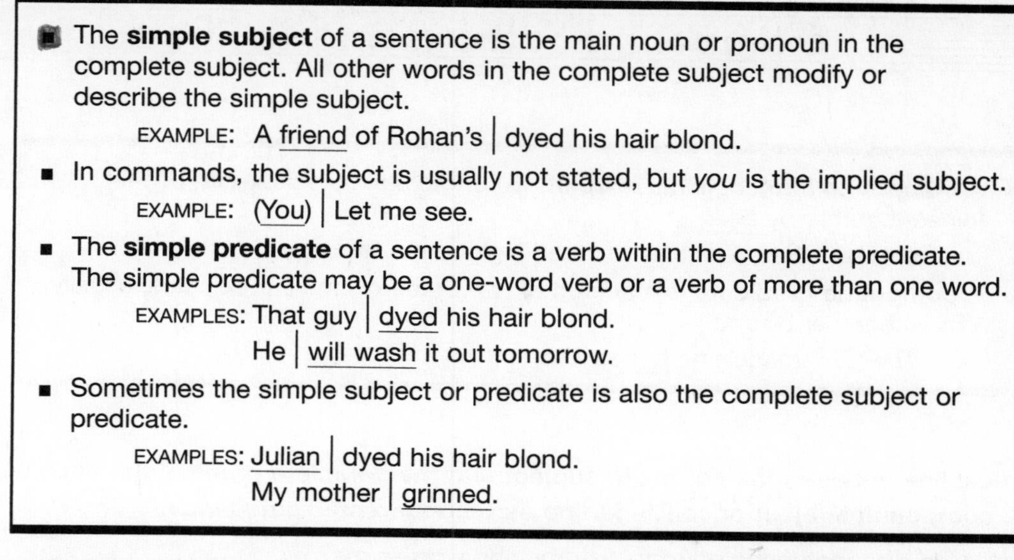

- The **simple subject** of a sentence is the main noun or pronoun in the complete subject. All other words in the complete subject modify or describe the simple subject.

  EXAMPLE: A friend of Rohan's | dyed his hair blond.
- In commands, the subject is usually not stated, but *you* is the implied subject.

  EXAMPLE: (You) | Let me see.
- The **simple predicate** of a sentence is a verb within the complete predicate. The simple predicate may be a one-word verb or a verb of more than one word.

  EXAMPLES: That guy | dyed his hair blond.
  He | will wash it out tomorrow.
- Sometimes the simple subject or predicate is also the complete subject or predicate.

  EXAMPLES: Julian | dyed his hair blond.
  My mother | grinned.

C. Draw a vertical line between the complete subject and complete predicate in each of the following sentences. Underline the simple subject once and the simple predicate twice. If the subject is implied, indicate the simple predicate only.

1. James Bond movies | drive me crazy.
2. The school | will be closed this week.
3. My oldest friend | on earth might visit next month.
4. We | have not seen each other for three years.
5. Su Mei's | first ball landed out of bounds.
6. The walls | in my room | need painting.
7. Drum lessons | would cost very little at that school.
8. The last house | on the street has been sold.
9. Cover your mouth | while yawning, young man!
10. This trivia game | about Canada | is teaching me a lot.

D. Add words to the simple subject and simple predicate given below. Draw a vertical line between the complete subject and the complete predicate in your finished sentences.

1. Grandmother skated. My old Grandmother | skated across the ice.
2. Children sneezed. The little Children | all sneezed at the same time.
3. Rodents gnawed. The infected rodents | gnawed on moldy cheese.
4. My brother sneered. My older brother | sneered at me when I came home late.
5. The car screeched. The bashed up car | screeched to a hault.

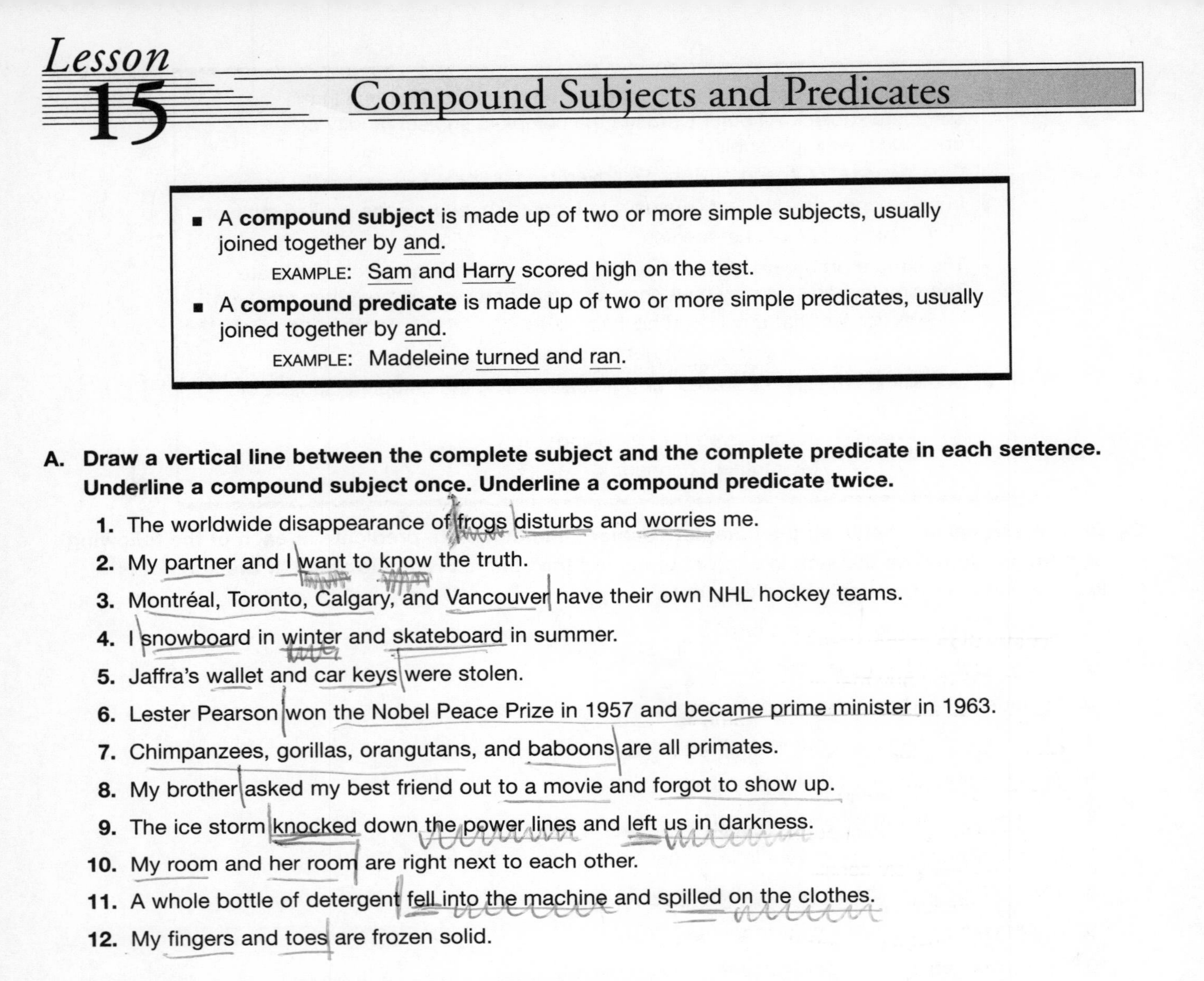

Lesson 15 Compound Subjects and Predicates

- A **compound subject** is made up of two or more simple subjects, usually joined together by and.

  EXAMPLE: Sam and Harry scored high on the test.

- A **compound predicate** is made up of two or more simple predicates, usually joined together by and.

  EXAMPLE: Madeleine turned and ran.

A. Draw a vertical line between the complete subject and the complete predicate in each sentence. Underline a compound subject once. Underline a compound predicate twice.

1. The worldwide disappearance of frogs | disturbs and worries me.
2. My partner and I | want to know the truth.
3. Montréal, Toronto, Calgary, and Vancouver | have their own NHL hockey teams.
4. I | snowboard in winter and skateboard in summer.
5. Jaffra's wallet and car keys | were stolen.
6. Lester Pearson | won the Nobel Peace Prize in 1957 and became prime minister in 1963.
7. Chimpanzees, gorillas, orangutans, and baboons | are all primates.
8. My brother | asked my best friend out to a movie and forgot to show up.
9. The ice storm | knocked down the power lines and left us in darkness.
10. My room and her room | are right next to each other.
11. A whole bottle of detergent | fell into the machine and spilled on the clothes.
12. My fingers and toes | are frozen solid.

B. Write four sentences containing compound subjects.

1. My Cat and her dog are friends.
2. Morgan, Emma and I have Drama this year.
3. You and I are very different.
4. Came with Dan and I.

C. Write four sentences containing compound predicates.

1. I jumped and screamed when I heard the news.
2. He ran and cried as he ran away.
3. I love and hate Highschool musical.
4. She fell and screamed as she was running.

Lesson 16

Direct Objects

- The **direct object** tells who or what receives the action of the verb. The direct object is a noun or pronoun that follows an action verb.

  EXAMPLES: Kiwi fruit contains **vitamin C**.
  Where did you put **my glasses**?

A. Underline the verb in each sentence, and then circle the direct object.

1. That guitarist has sold her CDs in almost every country on earth.
2. Daniel David Moses writes beautiful poetry.
3. Do you trust the information on that Web site?
4. The municipal government provides services to homeowners.
5. Our property taxes finance these services.
6. Why does Council oppose the development of a skateboard park?
7. Construction of the recreation centre will take months.
8. Where did you buy that unusual green hat?
9. I'm going to watch the hockey game on TV tonight.
10. Help your brother with his homework, please.
11. Did you slice the bread thinly?
12. Take a moment to reflect on Remembrance Day.
13. Have you seriously considered the offer?
14. The new auditorium can hold 1500 students.
15. My goldfish just had babies!
16. I lost my other sock at the laundromat.
17. Patel folded his hands on his lap.
18. The Toronto Raptors are facing elimination from the playoffs.
19. Adrianna's invention won first prize in the competition.
20. The person in the next seat was using both armrests.

B. Write five sentences containing direct objects. Circle the direct object in each sentence.

1. ______________________________
2. ______________________________
3. ______________________________
4. ______________________________
5. ______________________________

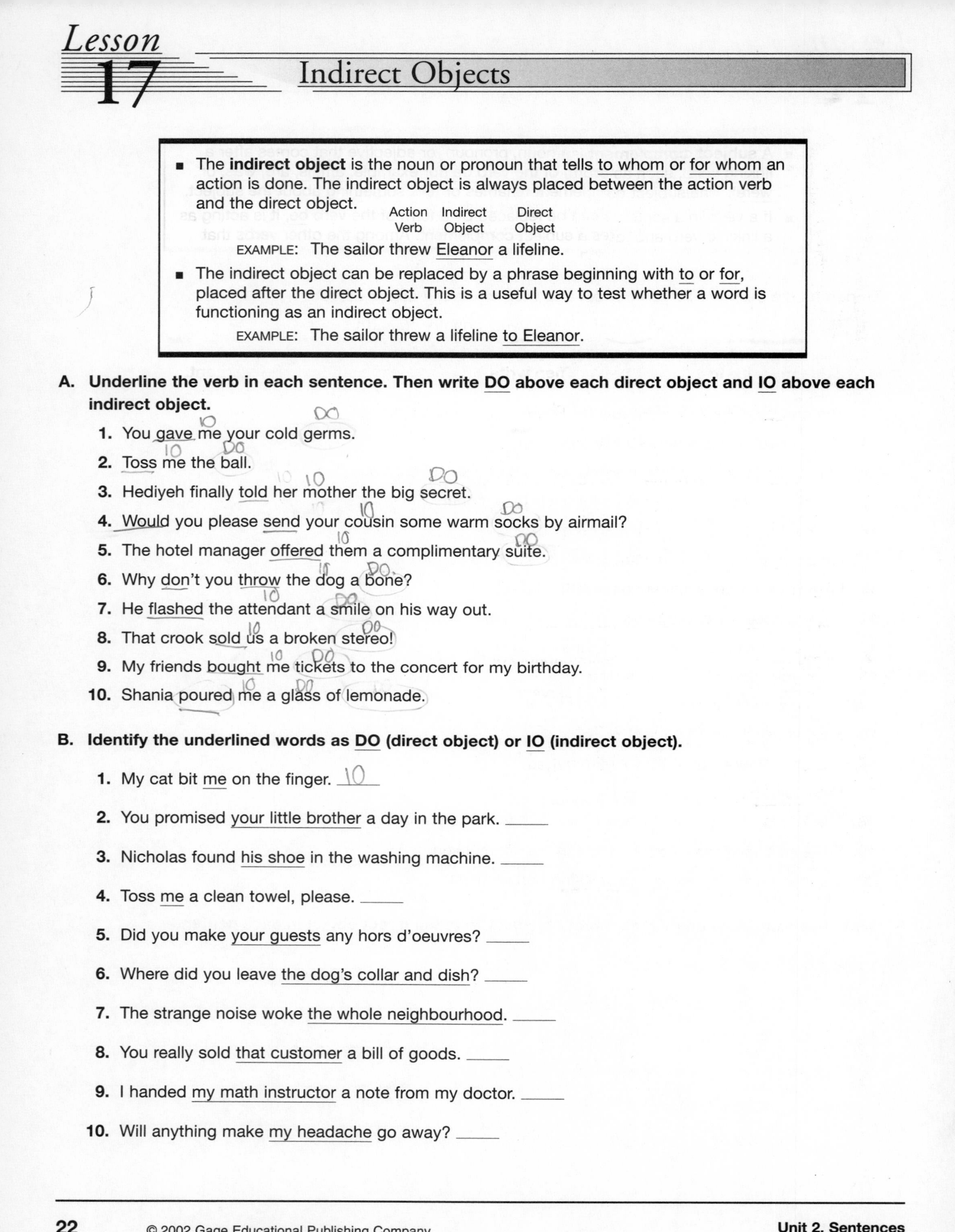

Lesson 17 Indirect Objects

- The **indirect object** is the noun or pronoun that tells to whom or for whom an action is done. The indirect object is always placed between the action verb and the direct object.

  EXAMPLE: The sailor threw (Action Verb) Eleanor (Indirect Object) a lifeline (Direct Object).

- The indirect object can be replaced by a phrase beginning with to or for, placed after the direct object. This is a useful way to test whether a word is functioning as an indirect object.

  EXAMPLE: The sailor threw a lifeline to Eleanor.

A. Underline the verb in each sentence. Then write DO above each direct object and IO above each indirect object.

1. You gave me your cold germs.
2. Toss me the ball.
3. Hediyeh finally told her mother the big secret.
4. Would you please send your cousin some warm socks by airmail?
5. The hotel manager offered them a complimentary suite.
6. Why don't you throw the dog a bone?
7. He flashed the attendant a smile on his way out.
8. That crook sold us a broken stereo!
9. My friends bought me tickets to the concert for my birthday.
10. Shania poured me a glass of lemonade.

B. Identify the underlined words as DO (direct object) or IO (indirect object).

1. My cat bit me on the finger. _____
2. You promised your little brother a day in the park. _____
3. Nicholas found his shoe in the washing machine. _____
4. Toss me a clean towel, please. _____
5. Did you make your guests any hors d'oeuvres? _____
6. Where did you leave the dog's collar and dish? _____
7. The strange noise woke the whole neighbourhood. _____
8. You really sold that customer a bill of goods. _____
9. I handed my math instructor a note from my doctor. _____
10. Will anything make my headache go away? _____

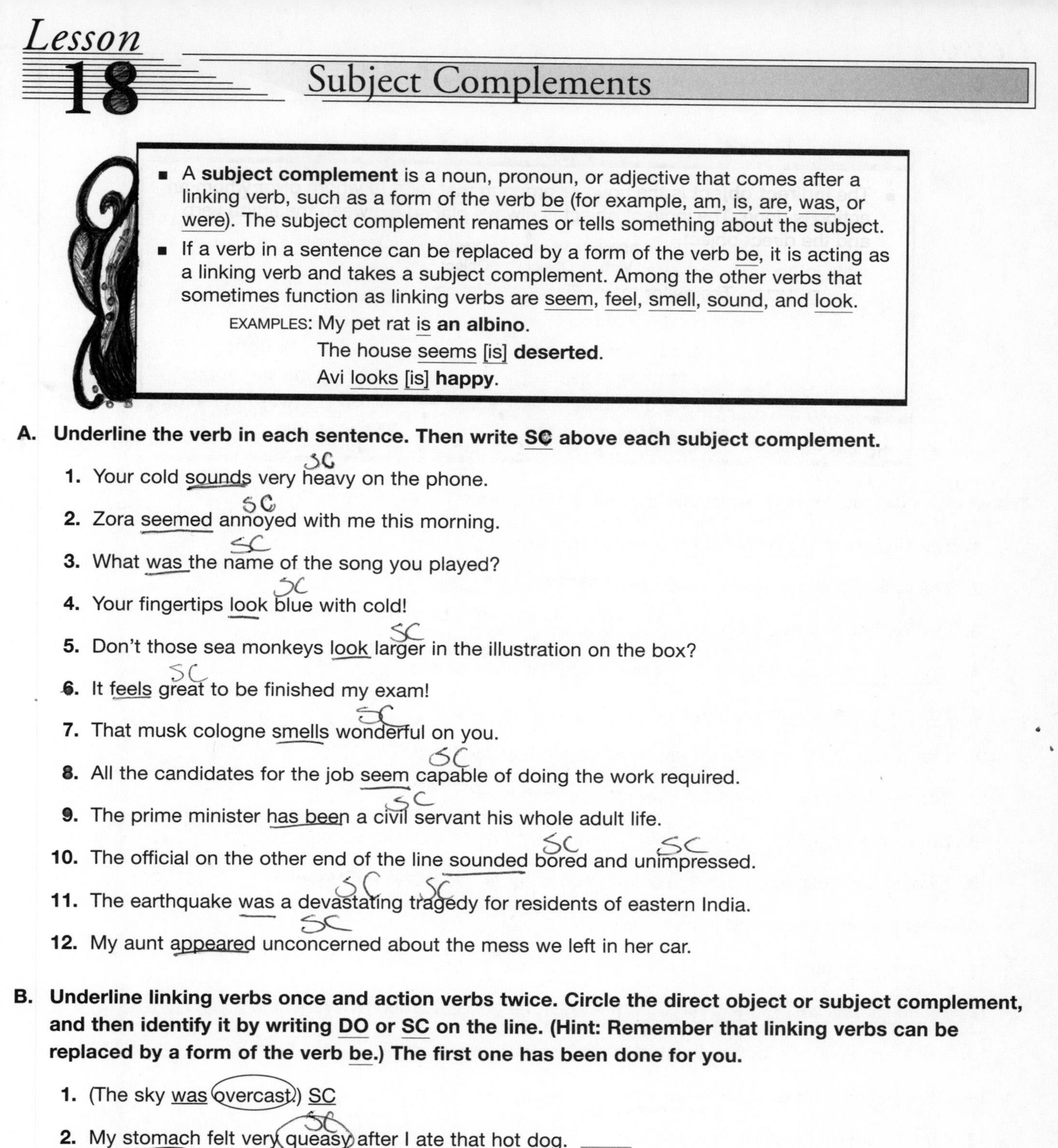

Lesson 18

Subject Complements

- A **subject complement** is a noun, pronoun, or adjective that comes after a linking verb, such as a form of the verb be (for example, am, is, are, was, or were). The subject complement renames or tells something about the subject.
- If a verb in a sentence can be replaced by a form of the verb be, it is acting as a linking verb and takes a subject complement. Among the other verbs that sometimes function as linking verbs are seem, feel, smell, sound, and look.

EXAMPLES: My pet rat is **an albino**.
The house seems [is] **deserted**.
Avi looks [is] **happy**.

A. Underline the verb in each sentence. Then write SC above each subject complement.

1. Your cold sounds very heavy on the phone.
2. Zora seemed annoyed with me this morning.
3. What was the name of the song you played?
4. Your fingertips look blue with cold!
5. Don't those sea monkeys look larger in the illustration on the box?
6. It feels great to be finished my exam!
7. That musk cologne smells wonderful on you.
8. All the candidates for the job seem capable of doing the work required.
9. The prime minister has been a civil servant his whole adult life.
10. The official on the other end of the line sounded bored and unimpressed.
11. The earthquake was a devastating tragedy for residents of eastern India.
12. My aunt appeared unconcerned about the mess we left in her car.

B. Underline linking verbs once and action verbs twice. Circle the direct object or subject complement, and then identify it by writing DO or SC on the line. (Hint: Remember that linking verbs can be replaced by a form of the verb be.) The first one has been done for you.

1. (The sky was overcast.) SC
2. My stomach felt very queasy after I ate that hot dog. _____
3. I could feel the grass tickling my chin. _____
4. Johanna looked dazed after the accident. _____
5. Robert smelled smoke somewhere in the basement. _____
6. The cake smelled delicious! _____
7. That cute little puppy will be a huge hungry dog in a few months! _____
8. Marta could feel the ground shaking during the earthquake. _____

Lesson 19 Phrases and Clauses

- Phrases and clauses are groups of words used in sentences. A **phrase** is a group of closely related words that function together as a single element, such as subject, verb, adjective, or adverb. A **clause** differs from a phrase in that it contains a <u>subject</u> and a **predicate**. Some sentences have only one clause, while others have several.

EXAMPLES:

Phrases	**Clauses**
Maria and Bai [subject]	whenever <u>I</u> **run**
should have won [verb]	that <u>Mimi</u> **bought**
with red hair [adjective]	<u>the boy</u> **ate the apple**
running through the field [adjective]	while <u>you</u> **were sleeping**
with passion [adverb]	<u>Babu</u> **is lost**

Tell whether the underlined words are a phrase or a clause.

1. The skylight <u>in the bathroom</u> is leaking. ____________
2. The novels <u>that you like to read</u> are really trashy! ____________
3. I've lost the key <u>to my house</u>. ____________
4. <u>Cory left his music playing</u> in his room with the door locked. ____________
5. I'd love <u>to have a great, big, creamy milkshake</u> right now. ____________
6. Marlie and Declan <u>had to be escorted</u> from the movie theatre. ____________
7. The windows <u>that you washed</u> are cleaner than mine. ____________
8. Kapuskasing, <u>which is in Northern Ontario</u>, gets lots of snow in winter. ____________
9. <u>I would have expected</u> more people to come out to see the Prime Minister. ____________
10. <u>Talking to my best friend</u> makes me happy. ____________
11. <u>Running through the forest</u>, Hiroshi got scratched by branches. ____________
12. <u>When Hiroshi was running through the forest</u>, he got scratched by branches. ____________
13. Canada's economy depends <u>on its abundant natural resources</u>. ____________
14. After panning for gold for years, <u>my uncle finally struck it rich</u>. ____________
15. I found myself <u>laughing uproariously</u>. ____________
16. When we were kids, we were afraid <u>to dive off the dock</u>. ____________
17. <u>Trembling with fear</u>, we would peer over the edge into the murky water. ____________
18. We believed <u>that a giant fish was lurking down there</u>. ____________
19. It was always hungry and wanted <u>to devour us</u>. ____________
20. We thought we could see its eyes <u>gleaming brightly</u>, staring up at us out of the depths. ____________

Lesson 20

Independent and Subordinate Clauses

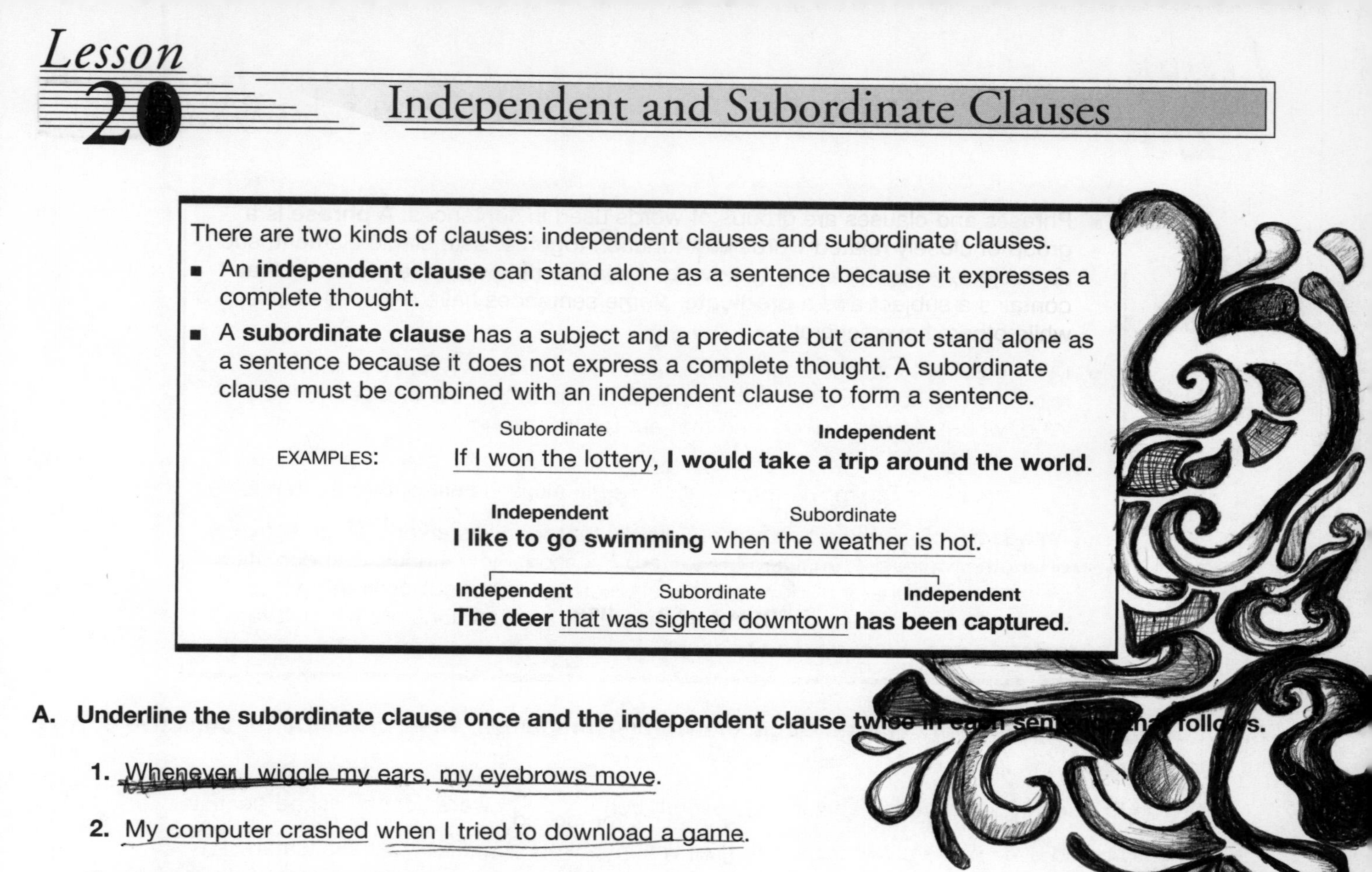

There are two kinds of clauses: independent clauses and subordinate clauses.

- An **independent clause** can stand alone as a sentence because it expresses a complete thought.
- A **subordinate clause** has a subject and a predicate but cannot stand alone as a sentence because it does not express a complete thought. A subordinate clause must be combined with an independent clause to form a sentence.

EXAMPLES:

Subordinate / **Independent**
If I won the lottery, **I would take a trip around the world.**

Independent / Subordinate
I like to go swimming when the weather is hot.

Independent / Subordinate / **Independent**
The deer that was sighted downtown **has been captured.**

A. Underline the subordinate clause once and the independent clause twice in each sentence that follows.

1. Whenever I wiggle my ears, my eyebrows move.
2. My computer crashed when I tried to download a game.
3. Hannah thanked the man who sold us the tickets.
4. I left my wallet in my bag, which is on the dining-room table at home.
5. My heart starts to beat faster when I think of our narrow escape.
6. Since Danny doesn't know where our seats are, we probably won't find him at the show.
7. Raj was sorry that he had to go.
8. Before I added two cups of baking soda, I should have checked the recipe.
9. The books that I lost never showed up.
10. My running shoe kept falling off because the laces were missing.

B. Write five sentences with one subordinate and one independent clause. Underline the independent clause in each sentence.

1. ______________________________
2. ______________________________
3. ______________________________
4. ______________________________
5. ______________________________

Lesson 21 Adjective, Adverb, and Noun Clauses

- Subordinate clauses can act as nouns, adjectives, or adverbs in a sentence.
- An **adjective clause** is a subordinate clause that modifies a noun or a pronoun. It answers the adjective questions which one or what kind. It usually modifies the word directly preceding it.
- Most adjective clauses begin with a relative pronoun. A relative pronoun relates an adjective clause to the noun or pronoun that the clause modifies. Who, whom, whose, which, and that are relative pronouns.

Adjective Clause

EXAMPLE: The movie that we watched in class was about ecosystems.

- An **adverb clause** is a subordinate clause that modifies a verb, an adjective, or another adverb. It answers the adverb questions how, under what condition, or why. Words that introduce adverb clauses are called **subordinating conjunctions**. Among the many subordinating conjunctions are when, after, before, since, although, and because.

A. Underline the subordinate clause. Circle the word(s) it modifies. Then write ADJ for adjective or ADV for adverb on the line.

1. The Etruscans, who lived in Italy in the seventh century B.C., were accomplished dentists. ADJ
2. They could even make crowns and bridges, which looked remarkably sophisticated. ADV
3. For some reason, all this knowledge disappeared when the Middle Ages arrived. ADV
4. "Travelling dentists," who had no real skill at dentistry, would pull teeth in the marketplace. ADJ
5. It must have hurt, because they offered no anesthetic. ADV
6. In the seventeenth century, dentists began to use fillings that contained gold. ADV
7. Wood or porcelain dentures were used before modern materials became available. _____
8. They must have looked very false when you smiled. _____
9. Today we have drugs that reduce the pain of dental surgery. _____
10. I'd like to shake the hand of the person who invented anesthetic! _____

B. Add an adjective or adverb clause to each of the following main clauses to make a sentence. Write ADJ for adjective or ADV for adverb to identify the kind of clause you wrote.

1. The car took the corners beautifully. ____________________
2. An ancient cave was uncovered. ____________________
3. My father caught a bat. ____________________
4. The water seeped through the walls. ____________________

- A **noun clause** is a subordinate clause that acts as a noun in a sentence. A noun clause usually functions as a subject, direct object, or subject complement.

  EXAMPLE: **Subject:** Whoever shows up first will get the best choice of seats.
  Direct object: I want what he has.
  Subject complement: Skateboarding is what I love to do.

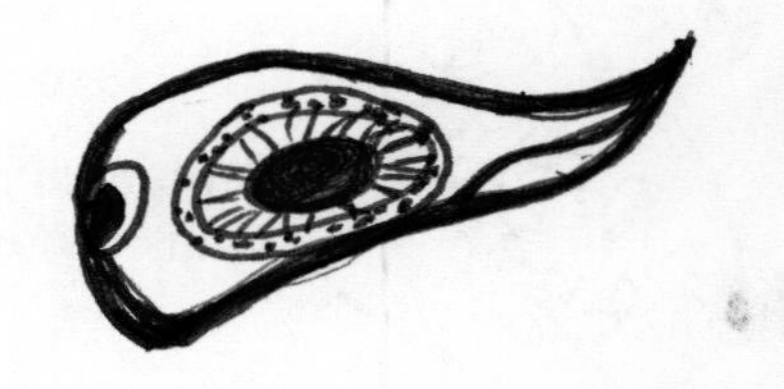

C. Underline the noun clause in each of the following sentences.

1. Whatever I do seems to turn out badly.
2. I believe that aliens crashed in the desert near Roswell, New Mexico.
3. They were eager for what had been promised them.
4. Mr. Malcolm figured out who was knocking over the garbage cans.
5. Happiness is what most people want.
6. That she refuses to hand over the evidence concerns me.
7. No one knows how they will repair the airplane.
8. I forgot what I came here for.
9. What we all need is a long holiday.
10. He asked how she got there.

D. Underline the subordinate clause in each of the following sentences. Label the clause ADJ for adjective, ADV for adverb, or N for noun.

hannah bailey

1. The dog that I grew up with was called Fido. _____
2. Whatever you decide will be fine with me. _____
3. He cried because somebody hurt him. _____
4. The bird chirped whenever I came near it. _____
5. I named my goldfish Flipper, in honour of a dolphin that had its own TV show. _____
6. Karin gave what she could spare to the panhandler. _____
7. People who live in glass houses should not throw stones. _____
8. Whoever wrote this is brilliant! _____
9. The building, which was designed by a famous architect, has attracted a lot of attention. _____
10. Stuart left early because he had to study. _____

Lesson 22

Simple, Compound, and Complex Sentences

- A **simple sentence** expresses a complete thought, using one independent clause.

  EXAMPLE: My cat dines on liver and onions. (Independent)

- A **compound sentence** expresses a complete thought using at least two independent clauses joined by a co-ordinating conjunction: and, or, nor, for, but, so, or yet. Each clause must have its own subject and predicate.

  EXAMPLE: My cat dines on liver and onions, but I eat macaroni. (Independent + Independent)

- A **complex sentence** expresses a complete thought using one independent clause and at least one subordinate clause.

  EXAMPLE: While my cat dines on liver and onions, I eat macaroni. (Subordinate + Independent)

A. Label each of the following sentences as simple, compound, or complex.

1. While I was eating lunch, I spilled my soup. ________
2. The girl in the red shirt has a very interesting voice. ________
3. My toes were numb, and my fingers were aching. ________
4. Before you drive to New Brunswick, check your route on the map. ________
5. Turn left at the corner, keep going straight, and turn right at the intersection. ________
6. Even if I'm starving, I will never eat canned luncheon meat again! ________
7. With light steps and a heavy heart, Bianca crept out the back door at the break of dawn. ________
8. Neither will I submit, nor will I give in. ________
9. Explain what you mean by that. ________
10. Samantha and Ali were hiking and snowboarding in the Rocky Mountains. ________
11. Clean up your room or I will dock your allowance! ________
12. A necklace with real pearls and a diamond in the centre hung around her neck. ________
13. The animal that I saw under the porch must have been a raccoon. ________
14. Six or seven passersby asked if they could help. ________
15. Please help me, for I am lost. ________
16. Neither of the girls has ever played hockey before. ________

B. Add clauses to the following simple sentences to create one compound and one complex sentence.

1. The students stared.

   Compound: The students started, and the hampster slept.

   Complex: when The students start the teachers drank their coffee.

2. The brakes failed.

   Compound: ____________________

   Complex: ____________________

3. The weather turned cold.

   Compound: ____________________

   Complex: ____________________

4. Zoltan likes video games.

   Compound: ____________________

   Complex: ____________________

5. My knee hurts.

   Compound: ____________________

   Complex: ____________________

C. Replace each of the following compound and complex sentences with three simple sentences.

1. I went to the store for milk, but it was closed, so I came home empty-handed.

   ____

   ____

   ____

2. Because I am feeling sick, I will eat lots of vegetables since they help the immune system.

   ____

   ____

   ____

3. I like eating chocolate, but my brothers always want some, and my mother makes me share.

   ____

   ____

   ____

4. If you want his autograph, come to the concert and ask him for it.

   ____

   ____

Lesson 23

Compound–Complex Sentences

A **compound–complex sentence** contains at least two independent clauses and at least one subordinate clause.

EXAMPLE: That house was sold (Independent), but we found another one (Independent) that we liked (Subordinate).

A. Underline each of the independent clauses in the following compound–complex sentences once, and underline each subordinate clause twice.

1. I thought that Ms. Wickstead was in hospital, but here she is.
2. I bailed, Henri steered, and we both prayed that we would be rescued.
3. Anju is a hotel chef, so why don't you ask if she will cater your party?
4. English grammar is full of quirks, and although I enjoy it, it can be very frustrating!
5. Farley Mowat, who wrote *Lost in the Barrens*, knows how to create suspense, and his book kept me turning pages until the end.

B. Label each of the following sentences as compound, complex, or compound–complex.

1. Tony Hawk may be the greatest skateboarder who ever lived, but I'll beat him one day! ____________
2. Alejandra plays the drums in a rock band at night, and she attends school during the day. ____________
3. I like the whole album, but the song that really impressed me was the first track. ____________
4. If you want to be a pop star, you will have to be good at dancing and singing. ____________
5. Geoff screamed and yelled, although nobody could hear him. ____________

C. Write three compound–complex sentences. Underline each independent clause once, and each subordinate clause twice.

1. ____

____

2. ____

____

3. ____

____

Lesson 24 Combining Sentences

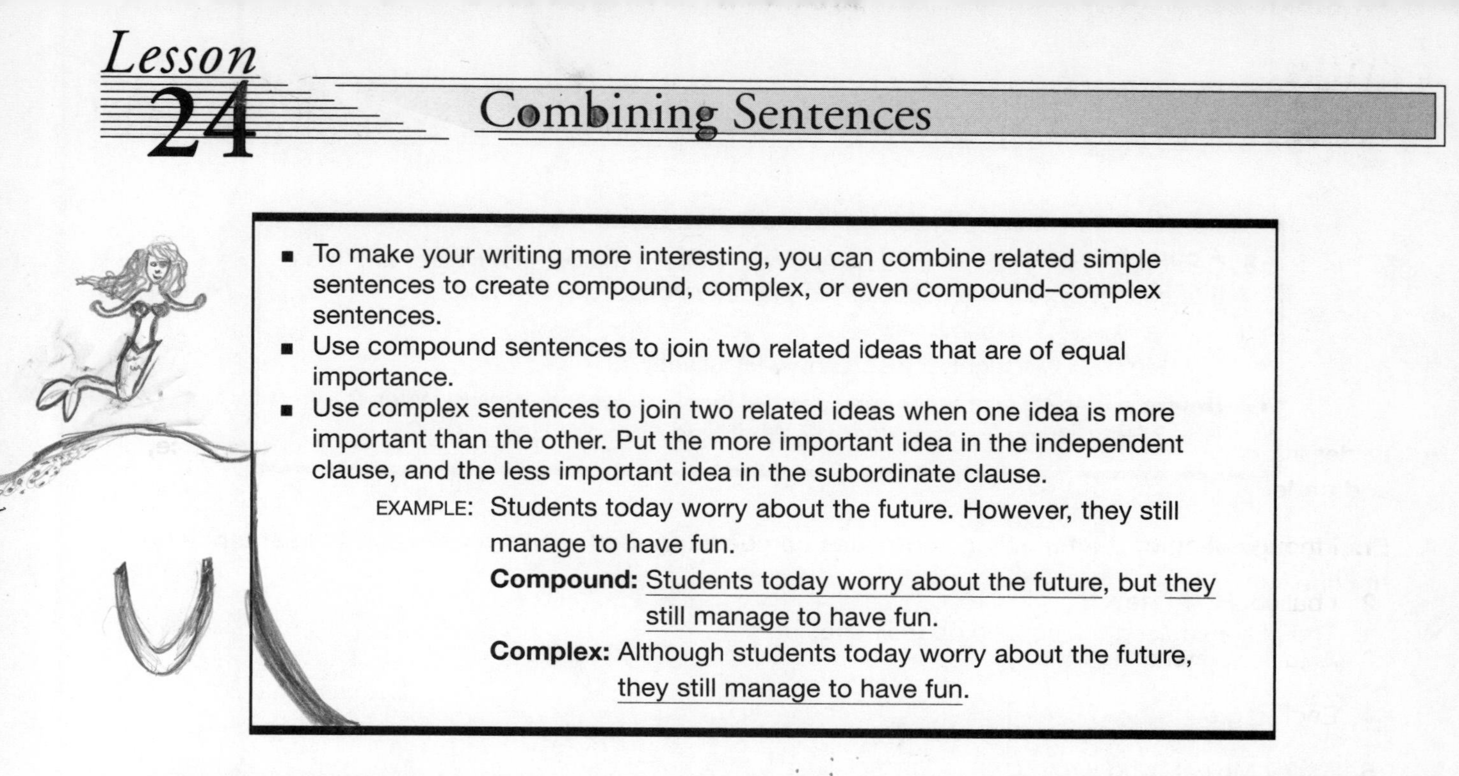

- To make your writing more interesting, you can combine related simple sentences to create compound, complex, or even compound–complex sentences.
- Use compound sentences to join two related ideas that are of equal importance.
- Use complex sentences to join two related ideas when one idea is more important than the other. Put the more important idea in the independent clause, and the less important idea in the subordinate clause.

  EXAMPLE: Students today worry about the future. However, they still manage to have fun.

  Compound: Students today worry about the future, but they still manage to have fun.

  Complex: Although students today worry about the future, they still manage to have fun.

A. Combine the following sentence pairs so that the underlined idea is emphasized. If both sentences are underlined, give both ideas equal emphasis.

1. I can't believe it. I lost my job.

____

2. I like to eat pizza. It makes my breath smell of garlic.

____

3. Next year I will be in the co-op program. I will be working at a local garage.

____

4. Many animals are endangered. They are losing their habitat.

____

5. Valentine's Day has come and gone. I didn't get a single card.

____

B. Rewrite the following paragraphs in your notebook. Combine sentences to improve the flow of the writing. Use at least one example of each of the following sentence structures: simple, compound, complex, and compound–complex.

Paleontologists were digging in Madagascar. They discovered a new dinosaur fossil. The dinosaur was about 2 m long. It weighed about 35 kg. It probably lived 65 to 70 million years ago. The dinosaur had unusual teeth. The front teeth pointed straight outward from the jaw. Scientists speculate about these teeth. What were they used for? They are not sure. They may have been used to catch fish, snakes, and lizards.

The scientists listened to music while digging. Their favourite music was by Mark Knopfler of the band Dire Straits. Therefore, they have called their dinosaur Masiakasaurus knopfleri in his honour.

Lesson 25 Expanding Sentences

- Sentences can be expanded by adding details to make them clearer and more interesting. Details are especially important in descriptive writing.

  EXAMPLE: The snow fell.
  All night, the soft snow fell silently.

- Details added to sentences may answer these questions: When? Where? How? How often? To what degree? What kind? Which? How many?

A. Decide how each of the following sentences can be expanded. Write your expanded sentence on the line.

1. The players raised the captain on their shoulders.

2. The lights flashed.

3. The protesters sat in the road.

4. Footsteps were heard.

5. The contestants had to eat bugs.

B. In your notebook, rewrite the following account of a fire, expanding each sentence by adding clarifying information or descriptive details. Be sure the account answers the 5Ws: who, what, when, where, and why.

A fire broke out at a factory. Firefighters arrived to find smoke billowing. Despite their efforts, the fire spread. Flames were visible. The heat forced firefighters back. All staff were evacuated. One firefighter was injured when a cylinder of propane exploded. The factory was destroyed. Police say they suspect arson. Company officials announced that they would rebuild the plant. Employees will be affected by the shutdown.

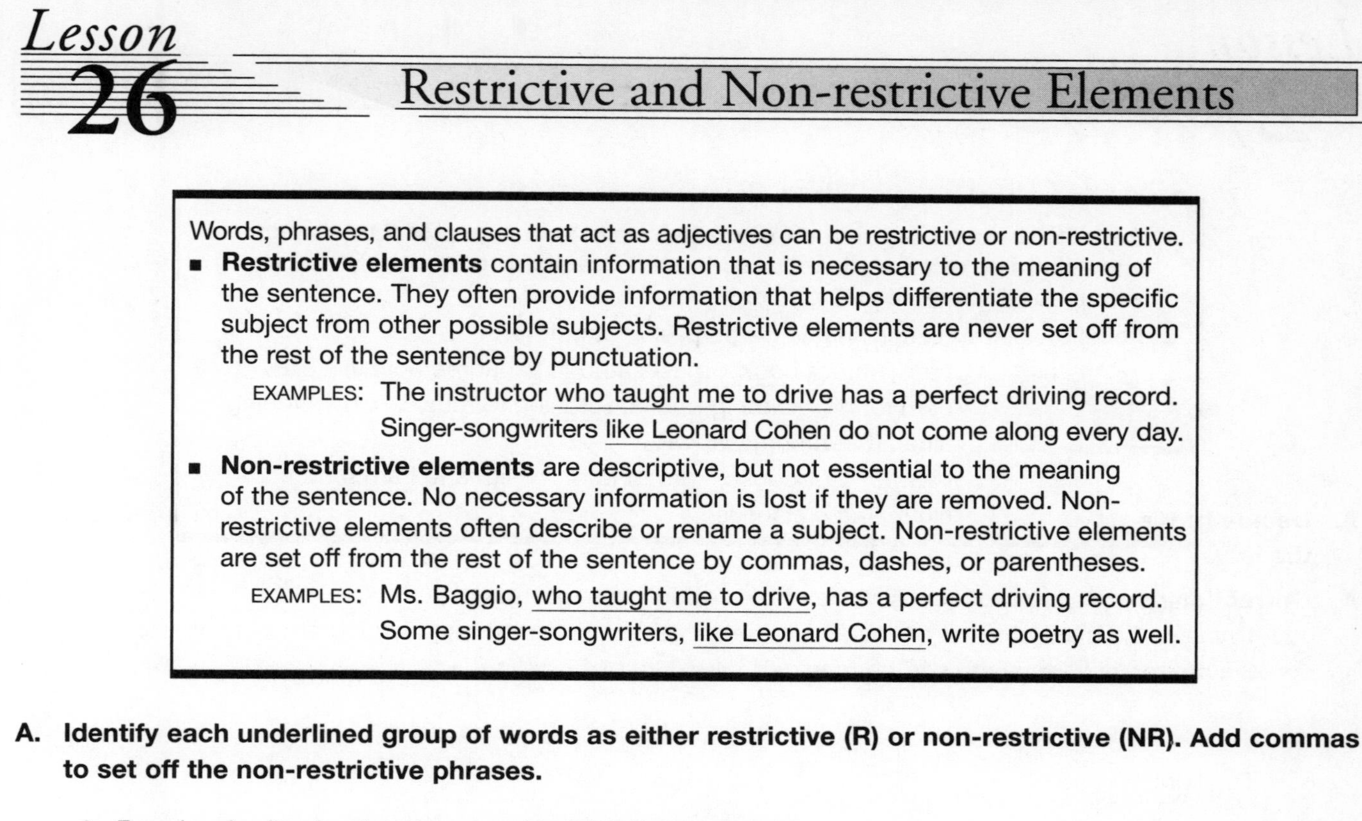

Lesson 26

Restrictive and Non-restrictive Elements

Words, phrases, and clauses that act as adjectives can be restrictive or non-restrictive.

- **Restrictive elements** contain information that is necessary to the meaning of the sentence. They often provide information that helps differentiate the specific subject from other possible subjects. Restrictive elements are never set off from the rest of the sentence by punctuation.

  EXAMPLES: The instructor who taught me to drive has a perfect driving record.
  Singer-songwriters like Leonard Cohen do not come along every day.

- **Non-restrictive elements** are descriptive, but not essential to the meaning of the sentence. No necessary information is lost if they are removed. Non-restrictive elements often describe or rename a subject. Non-restrictive elements are set off from the rest of the sentence by commas, dashes, or parentheses.

  EXAMPLES: Ms. Baggio, who taught me to drive, has a perfect driving record.
  Some singer-songwriters, like Leonard Cohen, write poetry as well.

A. Identify each underlined group of words as either restrictive (R) or non-restrictive (NR). Add commas to set off the non-restrictive phrases.

1. People who live in glass houses shouldn't throw stones. _____
2. My oldest brother Jerzy loves to snowboard. _____
3. The store at the end of the street sells fresh vegetables. _____
4. I lost my wallet which has my library card in it. _____
5. The children I was babysitting were already asleep. _____
6. Mr. and Mrs. Briscoe whose lawn I used to cut are moving. _____
7. My first dog Hercules was really hairy. _____
8. My hamster Ignace has an iron grip. _____
9. Your face had a look that I will never forget. _____
10. Asia the largest continent is home to more than half the world's population. _____

B. Underline the non-restrictive clause in each sentence that follows, and then add commas where necessary.

1. The polar ice caps which are sheets of ice that cover the North and South Pole are melting.
2. According to scientists, this is partly the result of human activity especially the burning of fossil fuels in cars and factories.
3. This phenomenon which is known as global warming will raise sea levels and cause widespread flooding.
4. Many low-lying areas such as Bangladesh may be covered by water.
5. Mr. Kuzak who works for Environment Canada explained what we can do to stop global warming.

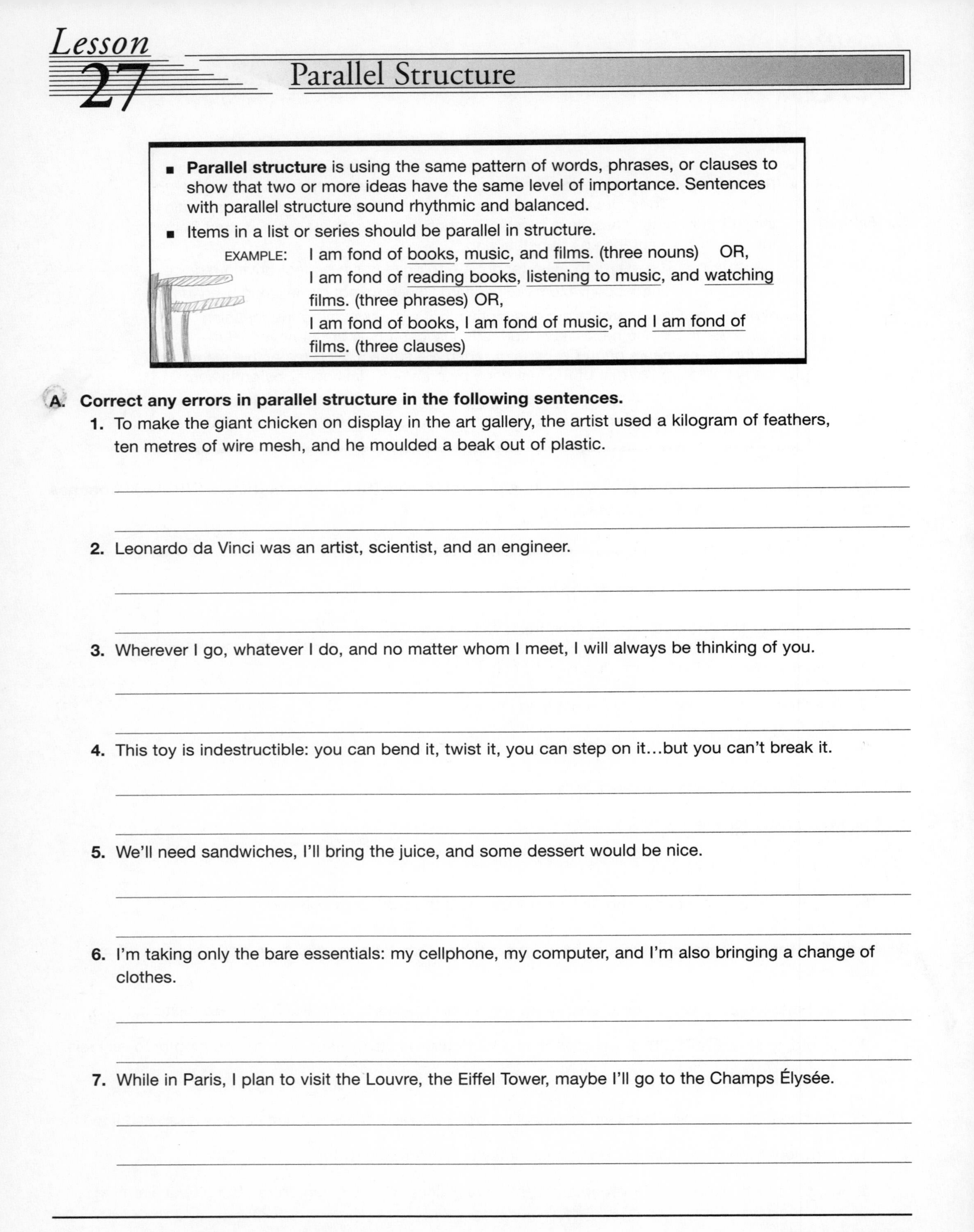

Lesson 27 Parallel Structure

- **Parallel structure** is using the same pattern of words, phrases, or clauses to show that two or more ideas have the same level of importance. Sentences with parallel structure sound rhythmic and balanced.
- Items in a list or series should be parallel in structure.

  EXAMPLE: I am fond of books, music, and films. (three nouns) OR,
  I am fond of reading books, listening to music, and watching films. (three phrases) OR,
  I am fond of books, I am fond of music, and I am fond of films. (three clauses)

A. Correct any errors in parallel structure in the following sentences.

1. To make the giant chicken on display in the art gallery, the artist used a kilogram of feathers, ten metres of wire mesh, and he moulded a beak out of plastic.

2. Leonardo da Vinci was an artist, scientist, and an engineer.

3. Wherever I go, whatever I do, and no matter whom I meet, I will always be thinking of you.

4. This toy is indestructible: you can bend it, twist it, you can step on it...but you can't break it.

5. We'll need sandwiches, I'll bring the juice, and some dessert would be nice.

6. I'm taking only the bare essentials: my cellphone, my computer, and I'm also bringing a change of clothes.

7. While in Paris, I plan to visit the Louvre, the Eiffel Tower, maybe I'll go to the Champs Élysée.

- In sentences with **correlative conjunctions**, such as **not only...but also**, **either...or**, **neither...nor**, and **both...and**, the words that follow each of the two conjunctions must be parallel in structure.

  EXAMPLE: Roberta Bondar was **not only** the first Canadian woman, **but also** the first neurologist to fly in the space shuttle.

B. Fill in the blank in each sentence with a parallel construction.

1. I will neither sign your petition ____________________
2. Savitsa is clever not only in math, ____________________
3. Shakespeare wrote both plays ____________________
4. Either help us move the couch, ____________________
5. It will either rain or ____________________ today.
6. Not only do Canadians love watching hockey, but also eating steaks
7. Both the lightbulb in my bedroom ____________________ have burned out.

- Use parallel sentence structures to link ideas or reinforce an important point in advertisements, persuasive writing, and oral presentations.

  EXAMPLE: Vote for honesty. Vote for decency. Vote for me.

C. Rewrite each of the following passages, using parallel sentence structure to reinforce the main point.

1. Students are responsible. They are willing to work, and minimum wage for students makes hiring them very affordable. So hire a student today.

____

____

2. Do you value the democratic right to freedom of speech? Maybe you want to announce something. Or is there an issue you think others should pay attention to? If so, then come on out to the You Said It forum in Sandborn Park.

____

____

____

3. Canada needs a leader who is willing to listen, but also willing to fight for what is right. In addition, our next prime minister should be someone with broad experience; she or he also needs a common touch, though. The leader must be a self-starter—but also a team player.

____

____

____

Lesson
28
Sentence Fragments

- A **sentence fragment** is a word or group of words, a phrase, or a subordinate clause that is punctuated as a complete sentence. Sentence fragments can be useful when used intentionally to create a specific effect (e.g., when writing dialogue, in advertising slogans, or as an answer to a question). However, unintentional sentence fragments should be avoided.

  EXAMPLE: **Fragment:** Try to exercise. Walking, running, or swimming.
  Corrected sentence: Try to exercise. You might enjoy walking, running, or swimming.

A. Label each of the following as either a sentence fragment (F) or a complete sentence (S).

1. Considering the state of the government these days. _____
2. Softly falls the night. _____
3. The results of the survey conducted last spring. _____
4. To have and to hold. _____
5. Canada's highest mountain, Mount Logan. _____
6. No, I'm not. _____
7. Of the ten major islands of the world, three of them are part of Canada. _____
8. Don't eat the glue! _____
9. Think about it before signing. _____
10. We get results. _____

B. Underline the sentence fragments in the following paragraph. Then rewrite the paragraph in your notebook, using complete sentences.

In the 1930s, world markets collapsed. Plunging countries into financial chaos. The Great Depression. Thousands of people lost their jobs, their homes. Everything. Unemployed men roamed the country looking for a handout in exchange for their labour. These hobos developed their own system of signs and symbols. Which they scratched with chalk on gateposts, trees, or sidewalks. Even, sometimes, marked on car tires. The signs gave hints and advance warning of trouble or help ahead. For example, a sympathetic woman was symbolized by a smiling cat. A man with a gun—a triangle with two raised hands. The symbol for danger, a long rectangle with a dot in the middle. Difficult though it was, the hobos found solace in their shared experiences. Sitting together around the campfire in so-called "hobo jungles," telling tales about riding the freight cars, avoiding the railroad police, and surviving the harsh conditions in the government relief camps.

C. Look through magazines, newspapers, and other sources of advertisements to find at least two different examples of sentence fragments used in advertising slogans. Write them in your notebook, with an explanation of why you think each slogan is (or is not) effective.

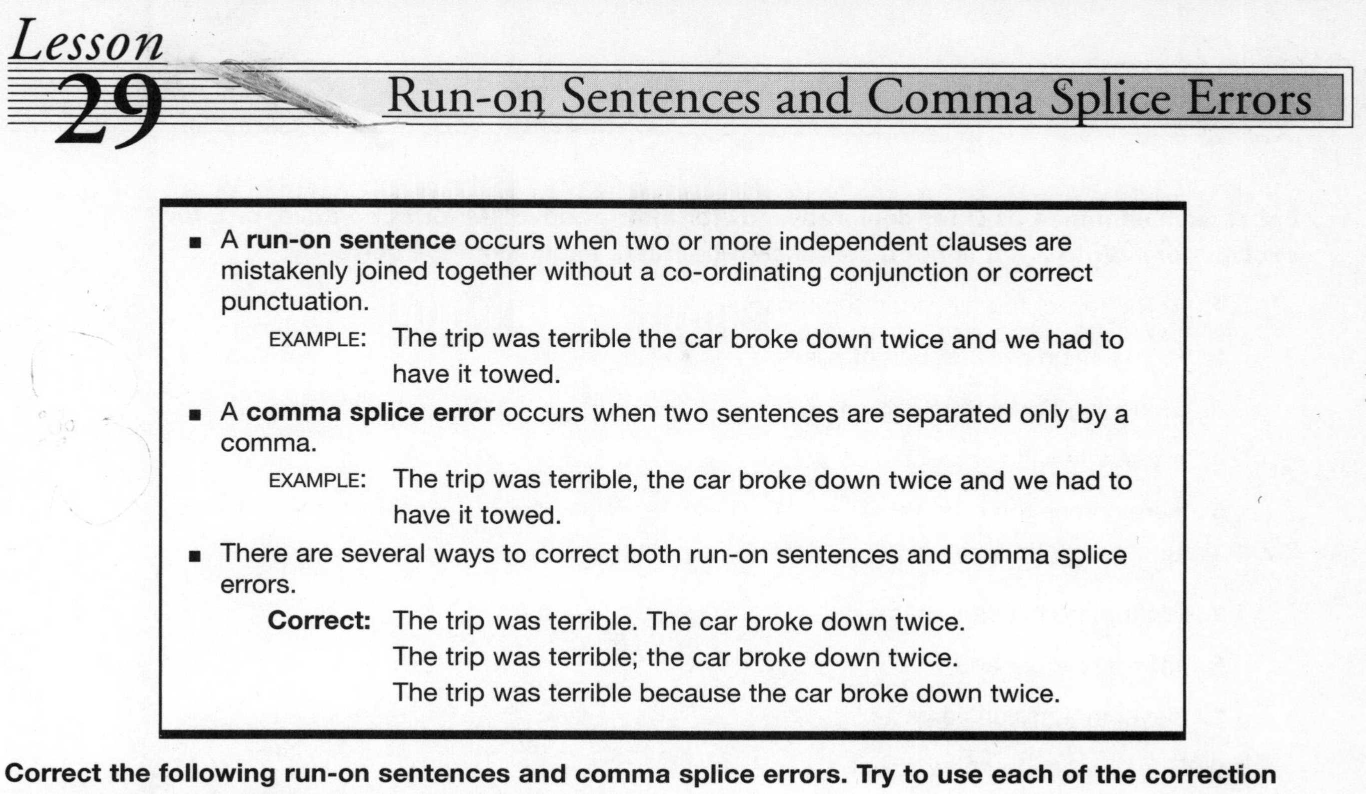

Lesson 29 Run-on Sentences and Comma Splice Errors

- A **run-on sentence** occurs when two or more independent clauses are mistakenly joined together without a co-ordinating conjunction or correct punctuation.

  EXAMPLE: The trip was terrible the car broke down twice and we had to have it towed.

- A **comma splice error** occurs when two sentences are separated only by a comma.

  EXAMPLE: The trip was terrible, the car broke down twice and we had to have it towed.

- There are several ways to correct both run-on sentences and comma splice errors.

  Correct: The trip was terrible. The car broke down twice.
  The trip was terrible; the car broke down twice.
  The trip was terrible because the car broke down twice.

Correct the following run-on sentences and comma splice errors. Try to use each of the correction methods described above in your answers.

1. The grass is soaked, the garden hose was left on too long.

   The Grass is soaked because the Garden hose was left on too long.

2. First we did some research then we built the model.

3. We went to the mall we were supposed to meet our friends all of us were going to see a movie together.

4. Margaret Atwood was at the conference so was Michael Ondaatje he gave a great speech.

5. Tumbler Ridge was once a coal-mining town however the mine closed, now the town is looking for new residents.

6. The sunrise was stunning, the sky was lit up with shades of red, we stood watching silently.

7. Watching Wayne Gretzky play hockey was like watching ballet on ice, he made everything look easy.

8. I'd love to go, however I'm working until nine that night.

9. Katina is a top skateboarder she has been practising all year.

10. Why would anyone go to horror movies they are so gross!

Review

A. Label each sentence as D for declarative, IN for interrogative, IM for imperative, or E for exclamatory. Write X if it is not a sentence. Punctuate each sentence correctly.

____ **1.** At the top of the hill stood the mosque ____

____ **2.** Please hand me that pair of pliers ____

____ **3.** Slouching home from school ____

____ **4.** Are you leaving so soon ____

____ **5.** Here comes the bus ____

____ **6.** Hooray, we won ____

____ **7.** What a great idea that is ____

____ **8.** Take a number and wait ____

____ **9.** Never in a million years ____

____ **10.** Does Fernando know about it ____

B. Identify five sentences from A that are in inverted order, and then, in your notebook, rewrite them as declarative sentences in natural order.

C. In each sentence below, underline the words that are identified in parentheses.

1. (simple subject) Since its introduction in the 1930s, television has transformed our world.

2. (simple predicate) Today, millions of people around the world watch television every day.

3. (indirect object) Popular TV shows give us a common basis of experience.

4. (complete predicate) In fact, popular culture could not exist without the mass media, including television.

5. (compound subject) Fads, fashions, and social trends become popular and are transmitted through television and other mass media.

6. (direct object) Lately, however, the Internet is challenging television's dominant position in North American society.

7. (compound predicate) More and more of us are going on-line and surfing the Net these days.

8. (subject complement) The impact this will have on society is hard to predict.

9. (simple subject) Surfing the Net is a much less passive activity than watching television.

10. (complete subject) The Internet, with its vast, unregulated sources of information, may create a more democratic society.

D. Underline the main clause once and the subordinate clause twice in each of the following sentences. Then identify the subordinate clause as a noun, adjective, or adverb clause.

1. The store where I bought my snowboard is having a sale. ________________
2. I believe that this is your book. ________________
3. Gun control has become an issue that divides Canadians. ________________
4. Ahmed sneezes whenever he goes outside. ________________
5. Because it was cold out, Kian shivered. ________________

E. Underline each independent clause once, and each subordinate clause twice. Then identify the following sentences as S for simple, CP for compound, CX for complex, or CPX for compound–complex.

1. Some of my classmates are going on a two-week exchange to Québec. _____
2. Each student will stay with a French Canadian family in a private home, and they will all meet every day for planned activities. _____
3. All communication during the trip will be in French, so students will get a chance to practise the skills that they have learned in French classes. _____
4. All sorts of outings are planned that will make the trip a memorable event. _____
5. Next month, the Québec students who are participating in the exchange will be coming here, and it will be our turn to show them our hospitality. _____

F. Identify the underlined word groups as a phrase or clause. Then describe their function in the sentence as restrictive (R) or non-restrictive (NR). The first one has been done for you.

1. My father, who works in an automobile factory, says he can get me a summer job. clause (NR)
2. This dog, for your information, is a great retriever! ________________
3. The singer with the gravelly voice has left the band. ________________
4. Maanav met the man whom he rescued from the fire. ________________
5. The world needs more people like Maanav. ________________

elevator love letter

G. Identify the error in each example below as SF for sentence fragment, RO for run-on sentence, or CS for comma splice. Then write a corrected version of each.

1. Water is important for life without it we could not last three days. _____

   ____

2. Is it an acid or a base, we need to check it with litmus paper. CS

   ____

3. Rowing as hard as they could, with the giant tsunami bearing down on them. X

   ____

4. Speaking of fishing, do you want to go now, I have another rod you could use. _____

   ____

5. I'd love to however I have to work. _____

   ____

Using What You've Learned

A. Read the sentences in the box. Then identify which sentence fits each description below.

1. Could I please take this book, which is mine?
2. I bought this bike because it looked cool, but it is not suitable for racing.
3. The gym that we had last year was old and this year it was replaced.
4. Pina just does whatever she pleases.
5. When you get back from the pool, give me a call.
6. Carl, go for breakfast right away, but the rest of you make your beds first.
7. Both Philip and Tan tried and failed to swim the lake.

____ (a) Imperative complex sentence with an indirect object

____ (b) Declarative compound–complex sentence with a subordinate adjective clause

____ (c) Declarative simple sentence with a compound subject and compound predicate

____ (d) Interrogative complex sentence with a non-restrictive subordinate clause

____ (e) Imperative compound sentence with a direct object

____ (f) Declarative compound–complex sentence with an adverb clause

____ (g) Declarative complex sentence with a subordinate noun clause

B. Write sentences that fit each description given below.

1. Declarative compound sentence with a direct object

____

____

2. Exclamatory simple sentence

____

____

3. Inverted interrogative sentence with a subject complement

____

____

C. For each of the sentences in the box in part A, underline the simple subject once and the simple predicate twice in each independent clause.

D. Underline the words or word groups that are parallel in the following sentences. Then tell whether they are words, phrases, subordinate clauses, or main clauses.

1. Come visit the Bahamas; come experience paradise. ________________
2. My head hurts when I cough, when I laugh, or when I try to read. ________________
3. My dog sleeps either in his bed or in mine. ________________
4. David Suzuki is an author, geneticist, and activist. ________________
5. When our neighbour plays his music, the floors shake, the windows rattle, and the dog hides under the piano. ________________

E. Expand each of the following sentences by adding details to make them more interesting.

1. The ship sailed. ____

____
2. The drill whined. ____

____
3. The competitors ran. ____

____

F. Rewrite the following passage in your notebook, combining sentences to improve the flow. Use at least one simple, one compound, one complex, and one compound–complex sentence in your final version.

Forest fires destroy habitat. They can cause a lot of damage. However, fires can also be beneficial. According to experts, land is laid waste in a fire. However, land is also regenerated by fire. Some plants and trees can only germinate in heat. They need a fire to propagate themselves. Other plants can't grow in densely forested areas. They need a lot of light to grow. The trees block the sun. Forest fires allow these plants to flourish. Many animals, such as deer and elk, love to feed on these plants. They, too, often flourish after a fire.

G. After each sentence in the passage below, write RO for run-on sentence, CS for comma splice, or SF for sentence fragment. Rewrite the passage in your notebook, eliminating these sentence errors.

Guess what some school boards are considering year-round schooling. _____ Instead of one long break in the summer, a three-week holiday at the end of each semester. _____ It may be hard for some of us to give up those long, lazy summers, however, the year-round system has many advantages. _____ Year-round schooling makes sense academically, administratively, and financially at least, that is what some people claim. _____ In the current system, students tend to forget much of what they learned, school boards must pay to maintain empty buildings during summer holidays. _____ On the other hand, no opportunities for students to gain experience in a full-time summer job. _____

Nouns

There are three classes of nouns in English.

- A **common noun** names any one of a class of objects.
  EXAMPLES: car school teacher
- A **proper noun** names a particular person place, thing, or idea. Proper nouns always begin with a capital letter.
  EXAMPLES: Ford Explorer St. Peter School Ms. Derewianko
- A **collective noun** names a whole class or group of objects.
  EXAMPLES: family flock multitude fleet team group

A. Underline each common noun once and each proper noun twice, and then circle each collective noun.

1. The class is going to Halifax next week.
2. Hard work is the secret ingredient in the success of the Pirates basketball team.
3. The new arena will be called the Leslie Clarke Arena, after our first coach.
4. The crowd watched, horrified, as the two players from Prince Edward Island collided.
5. Marcel has been called to be a member of the jury in that court case.
6. In childhood, the family is very important, and children's happiness can depend on the trust they have in their relatives.
7. The Cirque du Soleil came to town last night, and the whole town seems to be humming with excitement this morning.
8. The board of the West End Community Health Centre should exercise its authority by enforcing the rules.

B. Write a proper noun suggested by each common noun. Then use both the common noun and the proper noun in a sentence. Write the sentences in your notebook.

1. building ______
2. mall ______
3. painting ______
4. actor ______
5. celebrity ______
6. prime minister ______
7. country ______
8. songwriter ______
9. author ______
10. river ______

Nouns can be concrete or abstract.

- A **concrete noun** names something that can be perceived with at least one of the five senses.

  EXAMPLES: apple house smoke fur motor

- An **abstract noun** names an idea or quality that cannot be perceived by the senses.

  EXAMPLES: freedom courage anger honesty truth

C. Cross out the noun that does not belong in the same noun class as the others in the group. Then write the noun class (abstract, concrete, collective, or proper) that describes each series.

1. star, strength, muscle, captain ______________________
2. Parliament Buildings, magazine, *Maclean's*, *Time* ______________________
3. team, group, committee, player ______________________
4. revenge, justice, fear, judge ______________________
5. pride, litter, flock, sheep ______________________

D. Classify each common noun as concrete, collective, or abstract. Then write a sentence that shows the meaning of the noun.

1. religion ______________________
2. alien ______________________
3. herd ______________________
4. ethics ______________________
5. army ______________________
6. crew ______________________
7. scream ______________________
8. brood ______________________

Lesson 31 Singular and Plural Nouns

The following chart shows how to change singular nouns into plural nouns.

Noun	Plural Form	Examples
Most nouns	Add -s	king, kings; skate, skates
Nouns ending in a consonant and -y	Change the -y to -i and add -es	pony, ponies; navy, navies
Nouns ending in -o	Add -es or -s	potato, potatoes; piano, pianos
Most nouns ending in -f or -fe	Change the -f or -fe to ves	leaf, leaves
Most nouns ending in -ch, -sh, -s, or -x	Add -es	match, matches; rash, rashes; pass, passes; fox, foxes
Many two-word or three-word compound nouns	Add -s to the principal word	teaspoonfuls; governors general

Write the correct plural form for each singular noun.

A. **1.** beauty ________________

2. sheaf ________________

3. attorney ________________

4. responsibility ________________

5. cupful ________________

6. bus ________________

7. torpedo ________________

8. arrival ________________

9. solo ________________

10. carcass ________________

Exceptions to the basic rules for forming plurals include the following:

- Some words form plurals by changing their middle vowel sound.
  EXAMPLES: foot, feet louse, lice woman, women
- Some words have plural forms that are identical to their singular form.
  EXAMPLES: aircraft salmon species deer
- Some words that come from foreign languages retain their original plural form. Others have two accepted plural forms.
  EXAMPLES: alumnus—alumni; axis—axes; criterion—criteria; parenthesis—parentheses; cactus—cactuses or cacti; appendix—appendixes or appendices; radius—radiuses or radii

B. **1.** thesis ________________

2. swine ________________

3. mouse ________________

4. series ________________

5. cod ________________

6. basis ________________

7. oasis ________________

8. referendum ________________

9. phenomenon ________________

10. iris ________________

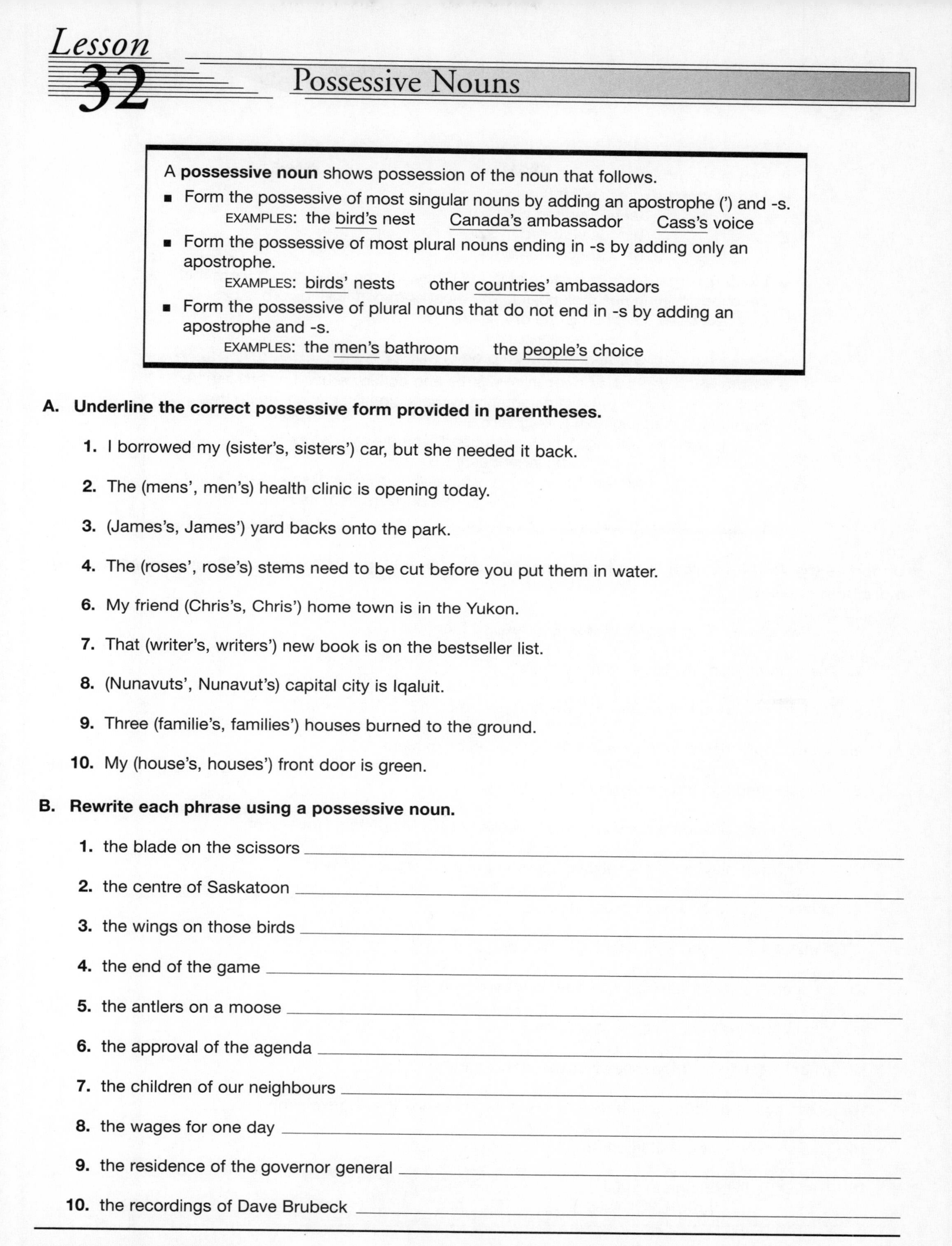

Lesson 32 Possessive Nouns

A **possessive noun** shows possession of the noun that follows.

- Form the possessive of most singular nouns by adding an apostrophe (') and -s.
  EXAMPLES: the bird's nest Canada's ambassador Cass's voice
- Form the possessive of most plural nouns ending in -s by adding only an apostrophe.
  EXAMPLES: birds' nests other countries' ambassadors
- Form the possessive of plural nouns that do not end in -s by adding an apostrophe and -s.
  EXAMPLES: the men's bathroom the people's choice

A. Underline the correct possessive form provided in parentheses.

1. I borrowed my (sister's, sisters') car, but she needed it back.
2. The (mens', men's) health clinic is opening today.
3. (James's, James') yard backs onto the park.
4. The (roses', rose's) stems need to be cut before you put them in water.
6. My friend (Chris's, Chris') home town is in the Yukon.
7. That (writer's, writers') new book is on the bestseller list.
8. (Nunavuts', Nunavut's) capital city is Iqaluit.
9. Three (familie's, families') houses burned to the ground.
10. My (house's, houses') front door is green.

B. Rewrite each phrase using a possessive noun.

1. the blade on the scissors ______
2. the centre of Saskatoon ______
3. the wings on those birds ______
4. the end of the game ______
5. the antlers on a moose ______
6. the approval of the agenda ______
7. the children of our neighbours ______
8. the wages for one day ______
9. the residence of the governor general ______
10. the recordings of Dave Brubeck ______

Lesson 33

Verbs

A **verb** is a word or group of words that expresses an action or a state of being.

- **Action verbs** express an action.

  EXAMPLES: Laetitia skated her best.
  Marcus watched in awe.
  We were cheering.

- **Linking verbs** describe a state of being. They link the subject to a word that describes or renames the subject. The most common linking verb is be.

  EXAMPLES: Stephen is the drummer.
  My old car was rusty.
  Our aunt has been promoted.

- Some verbs can act as both linking verbs and action verbs. If a verb can be replaced by a form of be in a sentence without significantly changing the meaning, it is acting as a linking verb.

  EXAMPLES: **Linking:** Mario looks good. The pie smells ready. The jar appears full.
  Action: Mario looks out the window. Sandi smells. the pie. The gopher appears from its hole.

Underline the verb (or verbs) in each sentence. Write L for linking or A for action. Some sentences have more than one verb.

1. Last week we sailed from Port-aux-Basques to Montréal. ________
2. The road felt slippery beneath the wheels. ________
3. The call resounded down the hallway and reverberated in the stairwell. ________
4. Agatha looks healthier in person than she does on camera. ________
5. We expected you to call before 5 p.m. ________
6. The escaped prisoners appeared three weeks later in Middleton, Nova Scotia. ________
7. The children played on the hillside, ignoring the calls of their parents. ________
8. My feet grew heavier with every step. ________
9. A friend will remain faithful through thick and thin. ________
10. It became obvious after a while that he wanted money. ________
11. Yuri felt for the light switch in the dark. ________
12. What happened in Moosonee last Saturday night? ________
13. Scraping the mud off your shoes before entering keeps the floors clean. ________
14. This chicken tastes a little off, don't you think? ________
15. That sounds like a great idea! ___

Lesson 34 Principal Parts of Verbs

- Three of the principal parts of a verb are the **present**, the **past**, and the **past participle**. The past participle is the form of the verb that is used after have.
- In regular verbs, the past and past participle forms are identical. In irregular verbs, however, these forms may differ.

EXAMPLES:	**present**	**past**	**past participle**
Regular	(I) love	(I) loved	I (have) loved
Irregular	(I) break	(I) broke	I (have) broken

- Dictionaries list irregular forms of verbs under the main entry for the verb. If no forms are listed, the verb is regular.

Fill in the chart below with the principal parts of the verbs listed. Check a dictionary if you are unsure about a particular verb form.

Base Form	**Present**	**Past**	**Past Participle**
1. agree	(I) ______	______	(have) ______
2. expect	(I) ______	______	(have) ______
3. think	(I) ______	______	(have) ______
4. go	(I) ______	______	(have) ______
5. drink	(I) ______	______	(have) ______
6. sit	(I) ______	______	(have) ______
7. freeze	(I) ______	______	(have) ______
8. read	(I) ______	______	(have) ______
9. swing	(I) ______	______	(have) ______
10. lead	(I) ______	______	(have) ______
11. bring	(I) ______	______	(have) ______
12. forget	(I) ______	______	(have) ______
13. become	(I) ______	______	(have) ______
14. begin	(I) ______	______	(have) ______
15. ring	(I) ______	______	(have) ______
16. run	(I) ______	______	(have) ______
17. ride	(I) ______	______	(have) ______
18. eat	(I) ______	______	(have) ______

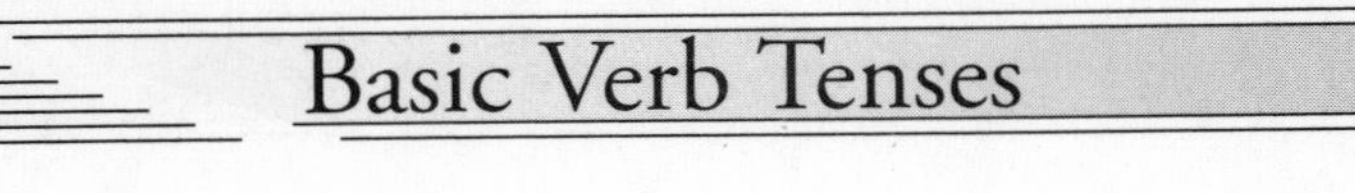

Lesson 35 Basic Verb Tenses

- Verb **tense** tells the time when the action or state of being occurred. The **present tense** tells what is happening now, the **past tense** tells about something that happened in the past, and the **future tense** tells about something that will happen in the future.

  EXAMPLE: **Present**: Sharla makes bread on Wednesday.
  Past: Sharla made bread on Wednesday.
  Future: Sharla will make bread on Wednesday.

A. Rewrite the following paragraph in the past tense.
I begin my journey by taking a plane to Athens. It rains every day for a week. Eventually, I pack it in and head by boat for Crete. The weather there is better, and I go swimming every day.

____

____

____

B. Rewrite the following paragraph in the present tense.
The film *Citizen Kane* began with the death of a wealthy newspaper magnate, Charles Foster Kane. Before he expired, the dying man whispered a single mysterious word—*rosebud*. The rest of the film presented flashbacks from the dead man's life, but the meaning of the word *rosebud* was not revealed until the very end of the film.

____

____

____

____

____

C. Rewrite the following paragraph in the future tense.
The new system serves two purposes. First, it allows companies to track financial records more accurately; second, it helps them to monitor the performance of each production team and assists senior managers to make useful comparisons. The result is a more efficient organization.

____

____

____

____

____

Other Uses of the Present Tense

The **present tense** is also used

- to express a general or scientific truth or belief;

  EXAMPLES: Canada's economy depends largely on its natural resources.
  All people are created equal.

- to describe a customary or repeated action or condition;

  EXAMPLES: Duane reads detective stories whenever he can.
  Sir Arthur Conan Doyle's last name is not hyphenated.

- in reviews or academic essays, to describe the characters or events in a film or literary work.

  EXAMPLE: Michael Ondaatje wrote *The English Patient*, which portrays a man torn between love and duty.

A. Rewrite the following sentences in your notebook, changing verbs to the present tense, where appropriate.

1. Christopher Columbus was among the first to assert that Earth was round.
2. In the seventeenth century, Newton proposed his first law: objects in motion stayed in motion until they were acted upon by another force.
3. Stuart soon found out that a watched pot never boiled.
4. J. R. R. Tolkien wrote *The Hobbit*, which told the story of Bilbo Baggins, who embarked on an adventure with Gandalf, the wizard.
5. In the story, Bilbo, Gandalf, and the dwarves tried to steal the treasure of Smaug the Magnificent, who was a huge and very evil dragon.

B. Rewrite the following paragraph in your notebook, making any changes to verb tense that are necessary for consistency and clarity.

Sir Arthur Conan Doyle was the creator of the fictional detective Sherlock Holmes. He wrote innumerable stories involving Holmes and his sidekick, Doctor Watson. However, Conan Doyle eventually grows tired of writing detective fiction. In *The Final Problem*, Holmes and his archrival, Professor Moriarty, engaged in hand-to-hand combat above the Reichenbach Falls in Switzerland. Both men plunged from the precipice and disappeared. The reaction of Holmes's fans to his death is outrage and Conan Doyle is eventually convinced to resurrect him. *The Empty House*, published in 1903, marked Holmes's return. In a famous scene from the story, Holmes explained to Watson how he fakes his own death in order to trick his adversaries.

Lesson 37 Present Perfect and Past Perfect Tenses

- The **present perfect** expresses an action or state that is completed at some indefinite past time, but which still applies in the present. The present perfect tense consists of has or have + the past participle.

  EXAMPLE: The Queen has visited Canada many times.
- The **past perfect** expresses some action or state that was completed before some other past action.

  EXAMPLE: We had already eaten when we arrived at the hotel.

A. Identify the tense of the underlined verbs as either present perfect or past perfect.

1. Mona has survived the operation, despite the odds. ____________
2. The people of Newfoundland and Labrador have always depended on the fishery. ____________
3. They had lived side by side for six years before meeting. ____________
4. Since Hillary and Norgay first reached the peak of Everest in 1953, over 400 climbers have made it to the top. ____________
5. The show had started, so we waited for a break before finding our seats. ____________
6. Before he was 23 years old, Alexander the Great had beaten the Persian army. ____________
7. Elvis has left the building. ____________
8. Traditionally, the Inuit have used inukshuks as landmarks. ____________
9. Josiah had completed three of the four assignments by the deadline. ____________
10. Photography has been around for over a century. ____________

B. Write the verbs in parentheses in either the past perfect or the present perfect.

1. I (tell) ____________ you a million times, I can't help you right now!
2. By the time the coast guard arrived, the ship (sink) ____________.
3. Dogs and cats (be) ____________ domesticated for thousands of years.
4. Bowling on St. Patrick's Day (become) ____________ a family tradition for us.
5. When we got there, the sale (end) ____________ .

C. For each verb listed below, write one sentence in your notebook in the present perfect tense and one sentence in the past perfect tense.

1. grow **2.** sail **3.** decide **4.** plunge

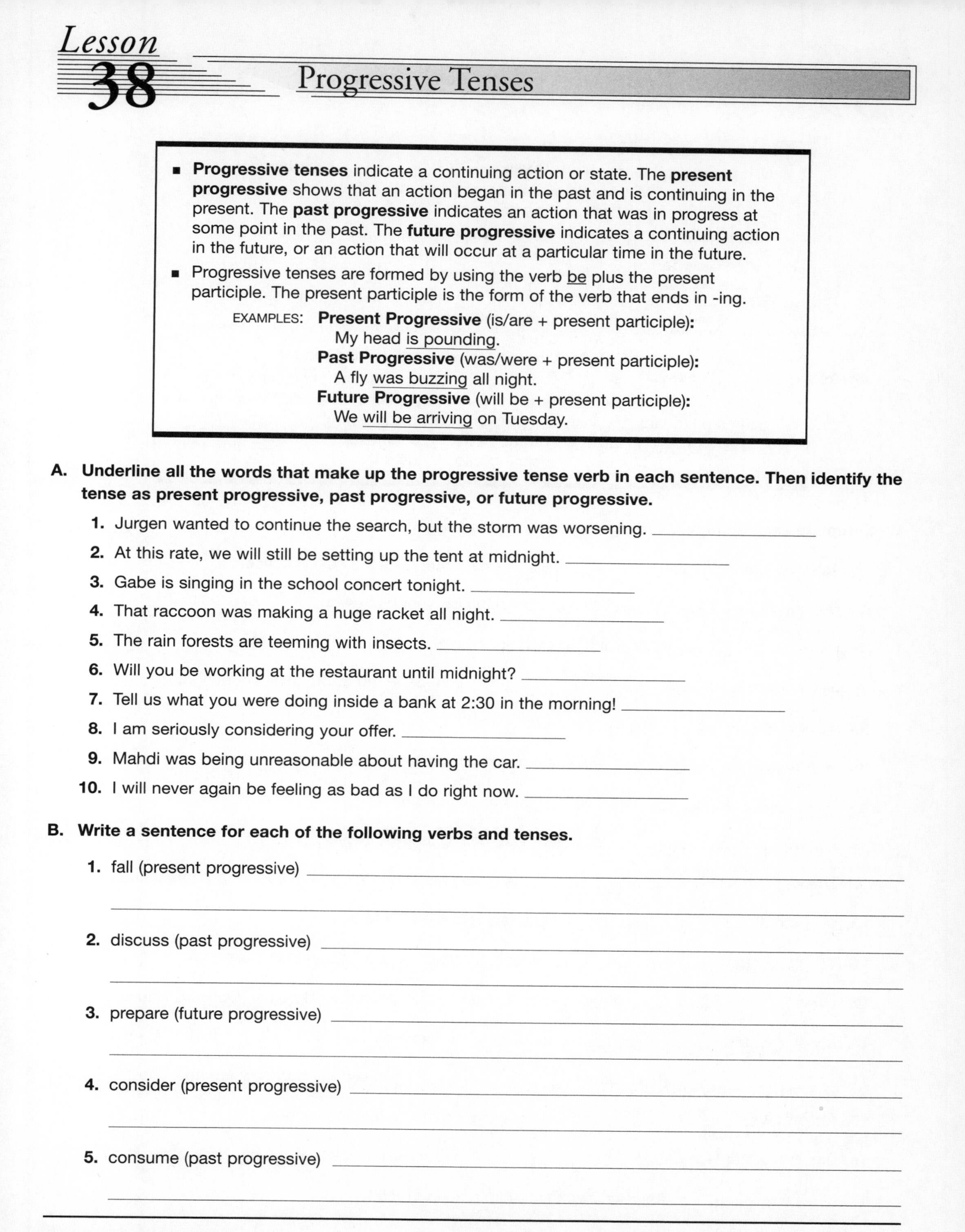

Lesson 38 Progressive Tenses

- **Progressive tenses** indicate a continuing action or state. The **present progressive** shows that an action began in the past and is continuing in the present. The **past progressive** indicates an action that was in progress at some point in the past. The **future progressive** indicates a continuing action in the future, or an action that will occur at a particular time in the future.
- Progressive tenses are formed by using the verb be plus the present participle. The present participle is the form of the verb that ends in -ing.

EXAMPLES: **Present Progressive** (is/are + present participle):
My head is pounding.
Past Progressive (was/were + present participle):
A fly was buzzing all night.
Future Progressive (will be + present participle):
We will be arriving on Tuesday.

A. Underline all the words that make up the progressive tense verb in each sentence. Then identify the tense as present progressive, past progressive, or future progressive.

1. Jurgen wanted to continue the search, but the storm was worsening. ____________
2. At this rate, we will still be setting up the tent at midnight. ____________
3. Gabe is singing in the school concert tonight. ____________
4. That raccoon was making a huge racket all night. ____________
5. The rain forests are teeming with insects. ____________
6. Will you be working at the restaurant until midnight? ____________
7. Tell us what you were doing inside a bank at 2:30 in the morning! ____________
8. I am seriously considering your offer. ____________
9. Mahdi was being unreasonable about having the car. ____________
10. I will never again be feeling as bad as I do right now. ____________

B. Write a sentence for each of the following verbs and tenses.

1. fall (present progressive) ____________
2. discuss (past progressive) ____________
3. prepare (future progressive) ____________
4. consider (present progressive) ____________
5. consume (past progressive) ____________

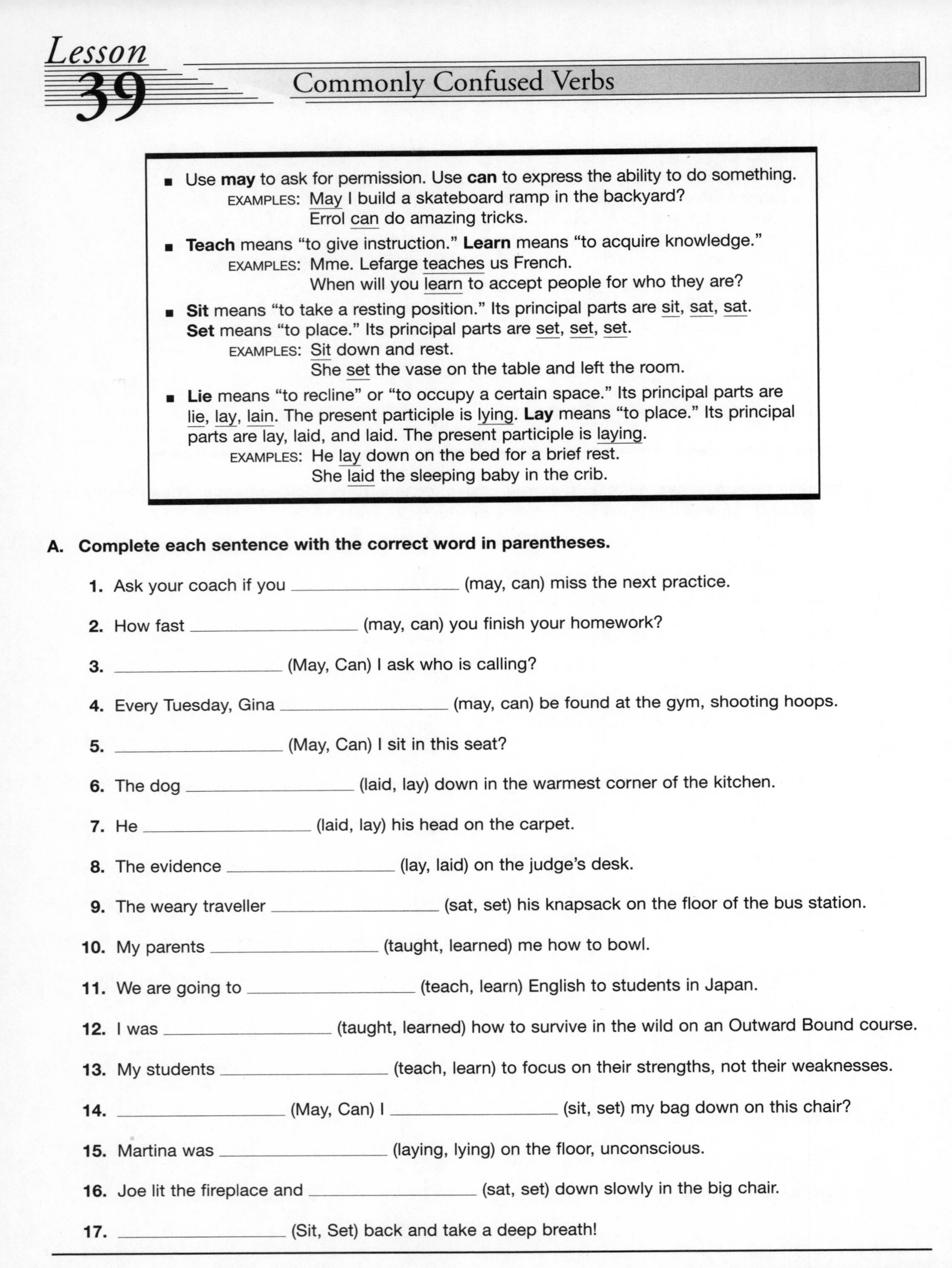

Lesson 39

Commonly Confused Verbs

- Use **may** to ask for permission. Use **can** to express the ability to do something.
  EXAMPLES: May I build a skateboard ramp in the backyard?
  Errol can do amazing tricks.
- **Teach** means "to give instruction." **Learn** means "to acquire knowledge."
  EXAMPLES: Mme. Lefarge teaches us French.
  When will you learn to accept people for who they are?
- **Sit** means "to take a resting position." Its principal parts are sit, sat, sat.
  Set means "to place." Its principal parts are set, set, set.
  EXAMPLES: Sit down and rest.
  She set the vase on the table and left the room.
- **Lie** means "to recline" or "to occupy a certain space." Its principal parts are lie, lay, lain. The present participle is lying. **Lay** means "to place." Its principal parts are lay, laid, and laid. The present participle is laying.
  EXAMPLES: He lay down on the bed for a brief rest.
  She laid the sleeping baby in the crib.

A. Complete each sentence with the correct word in parentheses.

1. Ask your coach if you ____________________ (may, can) miss the next practice.
2. How fast ____________________ (may, can) you finish your homework?
3. ____________________ (May, Can) I ask who is calling?
4. Every Tuesday, Gina ____________________ (may, can) be found at the gym, shooting hoops.
5. ____________________ (May, Can) I sit in this seat?
6. The dog ____________________ (laid, lay) down in the warmest corner of the kitchen.
7. He ____________________ (laid, lay) his head on the carpet.
8. The evidence ____________________ (lay, laid) on the judge's desk.
9. The weary traveller ____________________ (sat, set) his knapsack on the floor of the bus station.
10. My parents ____________________ (taught, learned) me how to bowl.
11. We are going to ____________________ (teach, learn) English to students in Japan.
12. I was ____________________ (taught, learned) how to survive in the wild on an Outward Bound course.
13. My students ____________________ (teach, learn) to focus on their strengths, not their weaknesses.
14. ____________________ (May, Can) I ____________________ (sit, set) my bag down on this chair?
15. Martina was ____________________ (laying, lying) on the floor, unconscious.
16. Joe lit the fireplace and ____________________ (sat, set) down slowly in the big chair.
17. ____________________ (Sit, Set) back and take a deep breath!

Lesson 40 Verbals: Participles, Gerunds, and Infinitives

- A **verbal** is a verb form that cannot function on its own as a verb. Three forms of verbals are **participles**, **gerunds**, and **infinitives**.
- The past participle and present participle can be used on their own as adjectives.
  EXAMPLES: **Past participle:** burnt toast frozen tundra
  Present participle: a laughing smile a running jump
- A gerund is a present participle that is used as a noun in a sentence.
  EXAMPLES: Running is hard on your knees.
  Irwin enjoys baking.

A. Underline the participle or gerund in each sentence. For each participle, circle the word it modifies.

1. Speaking slowly, the ambassador addressed the delegates.
2. The refining process for aluminum is quite complex.
3. Professor Dupuis handed me a torn sheet of paper.
4. I passed a wishing well and threw in a coin.
5. Our rapidly changing lives often contain a lot of stress.
6. Waiting in lineups drives me crazy.
7. Inez was a convincing recruiter for the school fundraiser.
8. Muhammad Ali made boxing look like an art form.
9. The stolen goods turned up in a pawn shop.
10. The audience was staring at the painted faces of the actors.

- The infinitive is the basic form of the verb, which is often preceded by to.
  EXAMPLES: to help to feel to come
- The infinitive can be used as an adjective, an adverb, or a noun.
  EXAMPLES: His will to live was very strong. (adjective)
  He was lucky to survive. (adverb)
  To err is human. (noun)

B. Underline the infinitive in each sentence, and then identify whether it is functioning as an adjective, adverb, or noun.

1. To win requires determination, intelligence, and planning. ________________
2. We worked hard to finish on time. ________________
3. We were pleased to meet your friend. ________________
4. The quickest way to get to Toronto is by train. ________________
5. To dine in that restaurant requires a reservation. ________________

Subject–Verb Agreement

- A verb must agree in number with its subject.

  EXAMPLES: The dog is barking. The cats are hissing.
- Difficulties with subject–verb agreement arise in the following instances:

Situation	Rule	Example (**subject** / verb)
Collective noun as the subject	Usually, use a singular verb.	The **jury** was out for three days.
Indefinite pronoun as the subject	Usually, use a singular verb, except with *both*, *many*, *few*, *others*, and *several*, which take a plural verb. *All*, *any*, and *some* can take a singular or plural verb, depending on the context.	**Everyone** is happy for you. **One** of the players is hurt. **Some** of the cake is left over. **Some** of the houses are sold.
Compound subjects connected by *and*	Usually, use a plural verb, unless the items form a single unit, or refer to the same person or thing.	**Haroun** and **Mihir** are knocking down a wall. **The soup and sandwich** is on special today. (single unit) **My oldest friend and best buddy** has moved away. (refer to same person)
Compound subjects connected by *or* or *nor*	Make the verb agree with the part closest to it.	*Either your job performance or your* **marks** are going to suffer. *Either your marks or your job* **performance** is going to suffer.

A. Underline the correct verb form.

1. Either John Williams or his sons (is, are) going to clear the snow for us.
2. Some of my credit cards (has, have) fallen out of my wallet.
3. Everyone who participated on school sports teams last year (is, are) going to receive a certificate for their efforts.
4. The committee looking into extra-curricular activities (is, are) meeting every Thursday.
5. Salsa and tortilla chips (has, have) replaced milk and cookies as my favourite snack.
6. Dean Martin and Jerry Lewis (was, were) a popular comedy team who made many movies in the 1950s.
7. My haven and refuge (is, are) my bedroom.
8. The sky, huge and blue and studded with small white clouds, (looms, loom) above us.
9. Either these instructions or my understanding (is, are) faulty.
10. All of my family (live, lives) in Cape Breton.

- When words separate the subject and the verb in a sentence, be sure to make the verb agree with the true subject.
  EXAMPLE: A pair of gloves was left in the snow.
  (subject is pair, not gloves)
- In sentences that begin with There is or There are, the verb agrees with the subject that comes after the verb, not with there.
  EXAMPLE: There are about 27 students per class.
  (subject is students)
  There is an empty classroom at the end of the hall.
  (subject is classroom)

B. Underline the subject and the verb in the following sentences. Write Y if they agree, and N if they do not agree.

1. The team with the most points get to move on to the next round. __________
2. The side effects of this potent drug is too dangerous for someone with a heart condition. __________
3. The insight into the foibles of human beings in Shakespeare's works makes him one of the greatest writers of all time. __________
4. The pages of the book on the top shelf is faded. __________
5. There are never a good reason to pick on someone. __________
6. There are both good and bad aspects to this deal. __________
7. There was, without a doubt, too many people in the room. __________
8. The large speakers on one side of the stage is giving feedback. __________
9. A battalion of soldiers, ready for action, was marching smartly along the road. __________
10. Both leaders of the scout pack that meets in the gym is sick tonight. __________

C. Complete the sentences below. Use a verb in the present tense that agrees with the subject.

1. The Singh family and I ____

____

2. The school band ____

____

3. The brochures he handed out during the seminar ____

____

4. A few of the participants at the conference ____

____

5. Neither the kittens nor their mother ____

____

Lesson 42 Active and Passive Voice

Voice refers to the relation of a subject to the action expressed by the verb.

- In the **active voice**, the subject does the action.
  EXAMPLE: The passengers tackled the hijacker.
- In the **passive voice**, the subject is acted upon. Form the passive voice by using a form of be (e.g., is, was, has been, will be) plus the past participle.
  EXAMPLE: The hijacker was tackled by the passengers.
- Use the passive voice when the doer of the action is unknown, unimportant, or obvious. In most other cases, use the active voice.
  EXAMPLES: A man was robbed near here last night. (unknown actor)
  The solution was heated to 130°C. (unimportant actor)
  The defendant was found guilty of murder. (obvious actor)

A. Underline all the words for each verb. Then write A for active or P for passive on the line.

1. I was raised as an only child. ____________
2. Yuen has found the lost bracelet. ____________
3. The crowd was yelling to the referee. ____________
4. This suit was dry-cleaned twice. ____________
5. The contaminated soil will be removed quickly. ____________

B. Rewrite each sentence in the active voice.

1. *The Canterbury Tales* was written by Geoffrey Chaucer in the fifteenth century.

____

____

2. Each of the tales is told by a different character.

____

____

3. Chaucer has been deemed by many scholars to be the first major English poet.

____

____

4. Many writers have been influenced by Chaucer's bawdy humour and insightful characterizations.

____

____

5. I think *The Canterbury Tales* can justifiably be called the most popular work in English literature.

____

____

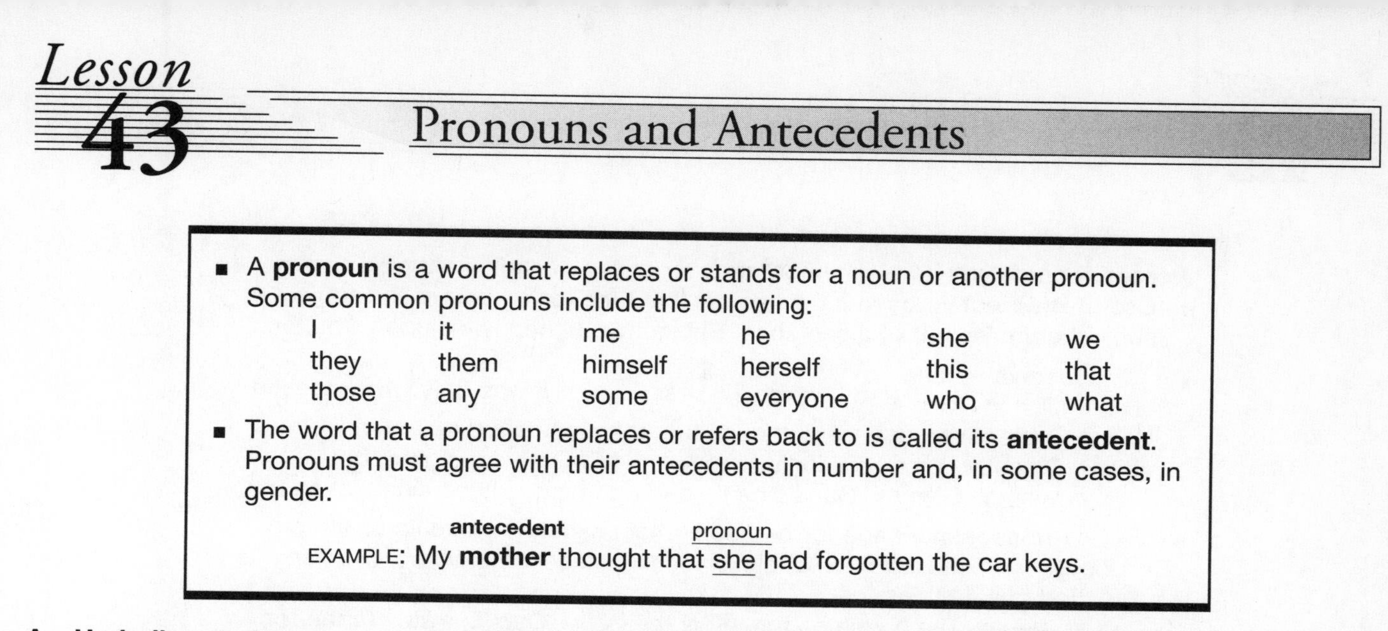

Lesson 43 Pronouns and Antecedents

- A **pronoun** is a word that replaces or stands for a noun or another pronoun. Some common pronouns include the following:

I	it	me	he	she	we
they	them	himself	herself	this	that
those	any	some	everyone	who	what

- The word that a pronoun replaces or refers back to is called its **antecedent**. Pronouns must agree with their antecedents in number and, in some cases, in gender.

EXAMPLE: My **mother** (antecedent) thought that she (pronoun) had forgotten the car keys.

A. Underline each pronoun and circle its antecedent. Connect pronoun and antecedent with an arrow.

1. Everett was not a person who enjoyed socializing.
2. The telephone has become more important as its role and capabilities have changed.
3. Amir's cellphone battery died because he forgot to recharge it.
4. Sarah gave herself a pat on the back.
5. The students in Judith's homeroom knew she was bound for glory.

- When one of the **singular indefinite pronouns** listed below is used as the antecedent to a pronoun, the pronoun must be singular.

everyone	everybody	someone	somebody
anyone	anybody	no one	nobody
each	either	neither	nothing

- In everyday conversation, the plural pronouns they, them, or their are often used to replace a singular indefinite pronoun. However, this is not acceptable in formal writing. Instead, use his or her, or change the subject to make it plural.

EXAMPLES: **Incorrect:** Everyone is responsible for their own belongings.
Correct: Everyone is responsible for his or her own belongings.
Correct: Passengers are responsible for their own belongings.

B. Underline the pronouns and their antecedents in the following sentences. Write Y if they agree, N if they do not agree.

1. Everyone driving a car is adding their contribution to global warming. ________
2. I believe that no one has the right to force their ideas on somebody else. ________
3. People in this city need to get their priorities straight. ________
4. Most candidates point with pride to the record of their leader. ________
5. Neither of the boys was eager to lose his place in line. ________

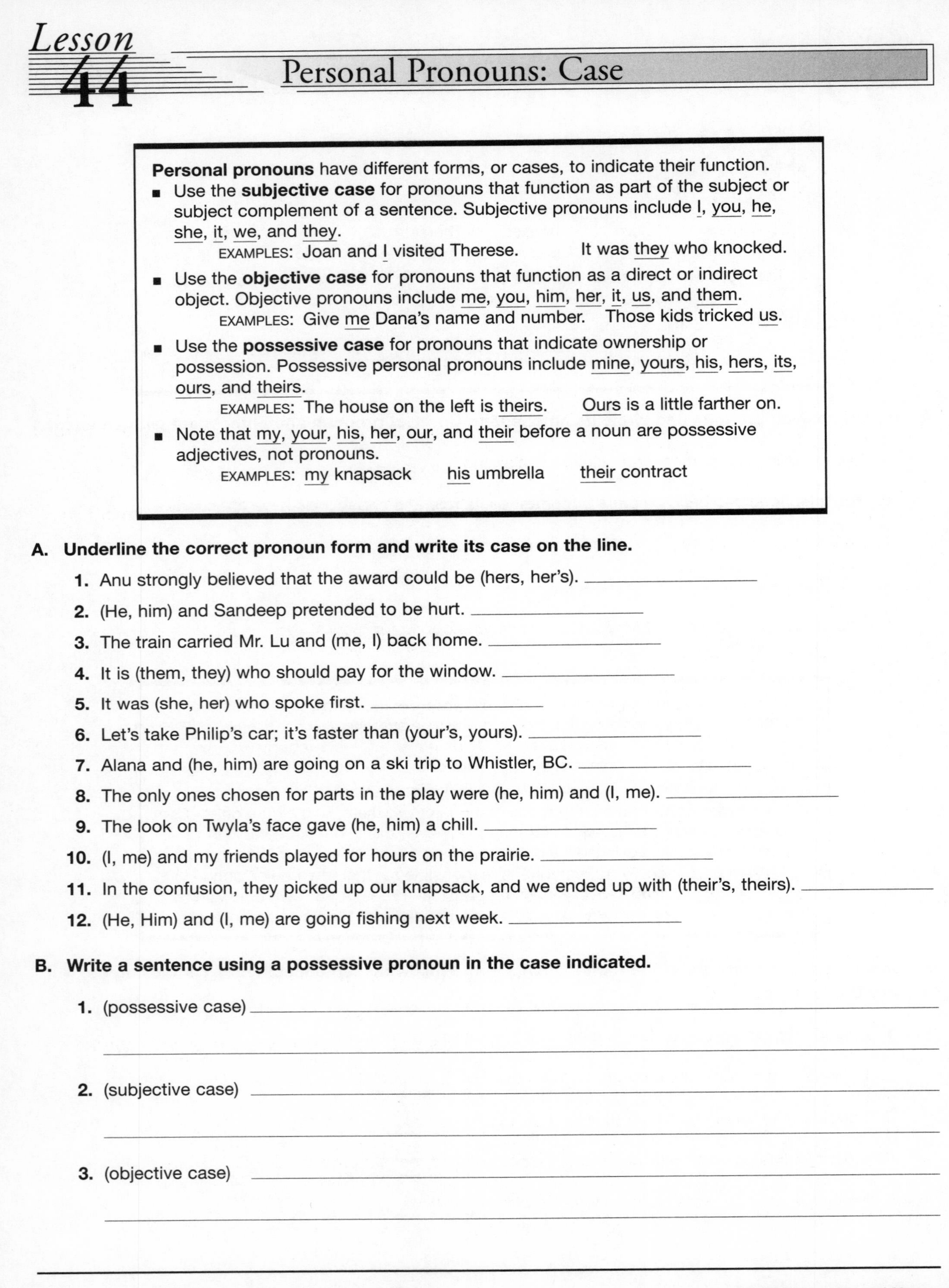

Lesson 44

Personal Pronouns: Case

Personal pronouns have different forms, or cases, to indicate their function.

- Use the **subjective case** for pronouns that function as part of the subject or subject complement of a sentence. Subjective pronouns include I, you, he, she, it, we, and they.
  EXAMPLES: Joan and I visited Therese. It was they who knocked.
- Use the **objective case** for pronouns that function as a direct or indirect object. Objective pronouns include me, you, him, her, it, us, and them.
  EXAMPLES: Give me Dana's name and number. Those kids tricked us.
- Use the **possessive case** for pronouns that indicate ownership or possession. Possessive personal pronouns include mine, yours, his, hers, its, ours, and theirs.
  EXAMPLES: The house on the left is theirs. Ours is a little farther on.
- Note that my, your, his, her, our, and their before a noun are possessive adjectives, not pronouns.
  EXAMPLES: my knapsack his umbrella their contract

A. Underline the correct pronoun form and write its case on the line.

1. Anu strongly believed that the award could be (hers, her's). ______________
2. (He, him) and Sandeep pretended to be hurt. ______________
3. The train carried Mr. Lu and (me, I) back home. ______________
4. It is (them, they) who should pay for the window. ______________
5. It was (she, her) who spoke first. ______________
6. Let's take Philip's car; it's faster than (your's, yours). ______________
7. Alana and (he, him) are going on a ski trip to Whistler, BC. ______________
8. The only ones chosen for parts in the play were (he, him) and (I, me). ______________
9. The look on Twyla's face gave (he, him) a chill. ______________
10. (I, me) and my friends played for hours on the prairie. ______________
11. In the confusion, they picked up our knapsack, and we ended up with (their's, theirs). ______________
12. (He, Him) and (I, me) are going fishing next week. ______________

B. Write a sentence using a possessive pronoun in the case indicated.

1. (possessive case) ______________________________
2. (subjective case) ______________________________
3. (objective case) ______________________________

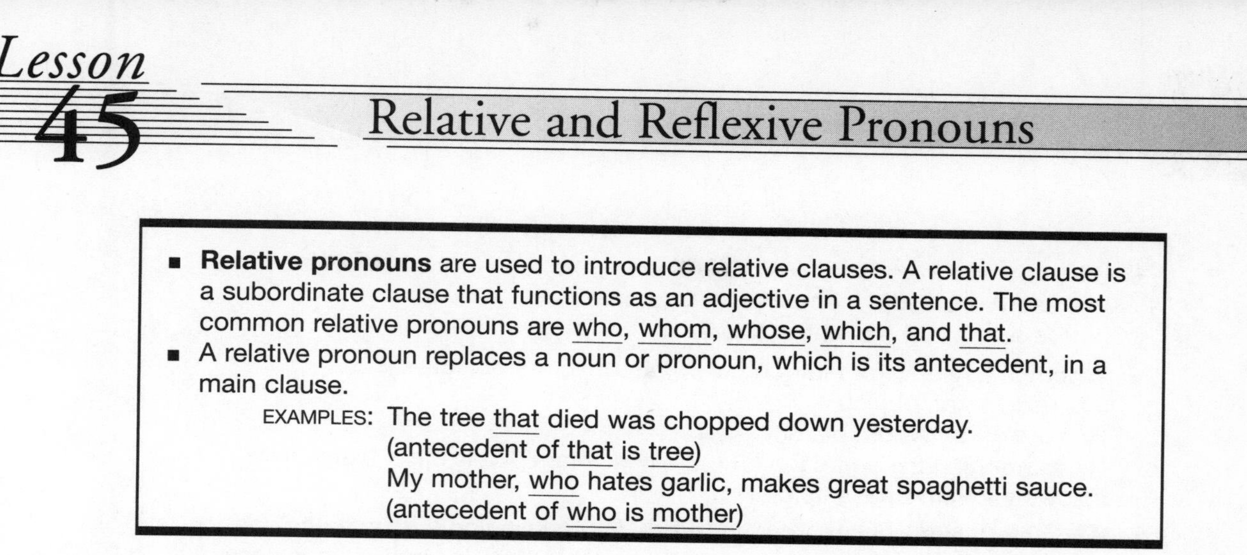

Lesson 45 Relative and Reflexive Pronouns

- **Relative pronouns** are used to introduce relative clauses. A relative clause is a subordinate clause that functions as an adjective in a sentence. The most common relative pronouns are who, whom, whose, which, and that.
- A relative pronoun replaces a noun or pronoun, which is its antecedent, in a main clause.

  EXAMPLES: The tree that died was chopped down yesterday.
  (antecedent of that is tree)
  My mother, who hates garlic, makes great spaghetti sauce.
  (antecedent of who is mother)

A. Underline each relative pronoun and circle its antecedent.

1. The hockey equipment in the gym, which includes new sticks and protective padding, has been well used.
2. A woman on the TV who claims to have psychic powers told them where the thieves were.
3. The influenza epidemic of 1918, which swept through Europe and North America just as troops were returning from World War I, claimed more lives than the war itself did.
4. "Wop" May, the famous Canadian bush pilot, got his nickname from a young cousin who could not pronounce "Wilfrid."
5. The film is playing in a theatre that was recently renovated.

- Use **reflexive pronouns** (myself, yourself, himself, herself, itself, ourselves, yourselves, themselves) to refer back to a person or thing that is the subject of the sentence.

  EXAMPLES: Kirsten cut herself a large piece of cake. (antecedent is Kirsten)
  The children laughed themselves silly watching that cartoon.
  (antecedent is children)
- Use reflexive pronouns immediately after a noun or pronoun to add emphasis.

  EXAMPLE: The Queen herself attended the ceremony.
  (antecedent is Queen)
- Do not use a reflexive pronoun in place of a personal pronoun.

  EXAMPLE: **Incorrect:** Shiva and myself went for a soda.
  Correct: Shiva and I went for a soda.

B. Write C if the reflexive pronoun is used correctly. Write X if it is used incorrectly, and then write the pronoun that should replace it.

1. Ira admits that he himself was responsible for the mess. ________________
2. I will give herself a call when I have a free moment. ________________
3. The Grade 10 students raised the money for the trip by themselves. ________________
4. My horse and myself took a victory lap around the enclosure. ________________
5. Mr. Stavros paid for his son Nico and himself to play tennis. ________________

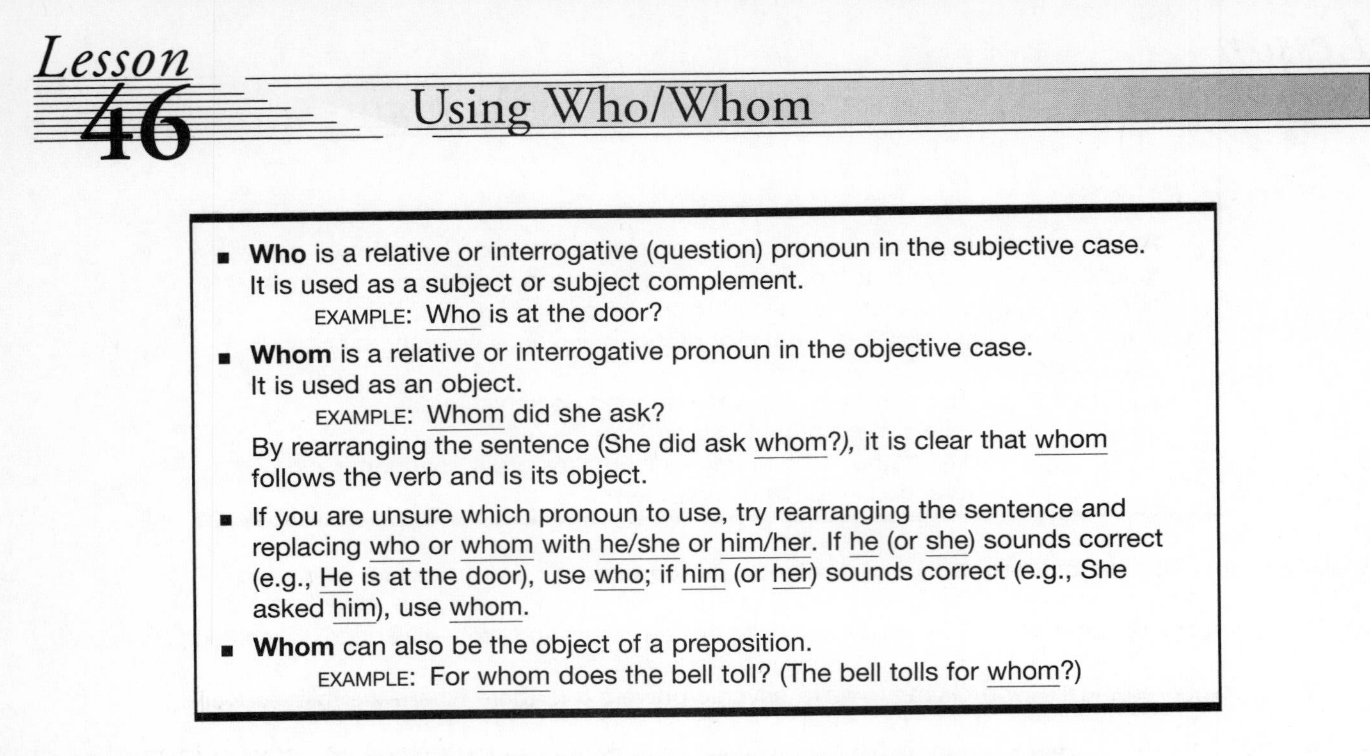

Lesson 46 Using Who/Whom

- **Who** is a relative or interrogative (question) pronoun in the subjective case. It is used as a subject or subject complement.
  EXAMPLE: Who is at the door?
- **Whom** is a relative or interrogative pronoun in the objective case. It is used as an object.
  EXAMPLE: Whom did she ask?
  By rearranging the sentence (She did ask whom?), it is clear that whom follows the verb and is its object.
- If you are unsure which pronoun to use, try rearranging the sentence and replacing who or whom with he/she or him/her. If he (or she) sounds correct (e.g., He is at the door), use who; if him (or her) sounds correct (e.g., She asked him), use whom.
- **Whom** can also be the object of a preposition.
  EXAMPLE: For whom does the bell toll? (The bell tolls for whom?)

A. Complete each sentence with the correct interrogative pronoun: who or whom.

1. ____________________ are you taking to Victoria?
2. ____________________ will we appoint as treasurer?
3. ____________________ has a quarter for a phone call?
4. ____________________ are the recruiters going to hire?
5. ____________________ could that possibly be?

- When who or whom are used as **relative pronouns**, rearrange the words in the relative clause to determine if the pronoun acts as a subject or an object.
  EXAMPLES: The man [who died] was wealthy.
  (who died—subject)
  The man [whom we visited] was German.
  (we visited whom—direct object)
  The player [whom we cheered for] was replaced.
  (we cheered for whom—object of preposition)

B. Complete each sentence with the correct relative pronoun: who or whom.

1. The lean and hungry fellow ____________________ Brutus was speaking with was Cassius.
2. The salesperson ____________________ I spoke with said we could pick it up on Friday.
3. The doctor ____________________ is treating my ulcer is on vacation.
4. That girl Miranda, ____________________ lives on an island, has fallen in love.
5. The king ____________________ Elizabeth I named as her successor was James I.

Lesson 47 Adjectives

- **Adjectives** describe, limit, or identify a noun or pronoun. A descriptive adjective adds detail or answers the question *What is it like?*
  EXAMPLES: blue eyes   lucky number
- A **limiting adjective** makes the noun or pronoun it modifies more specific and concrete. Some common limiting adjectives are few, many, every, each, both, several, some, any, most, and one. The limiting adjectives a, an, and the are called **articles.**
  EXAMPLES: few people   one day   an argument
- Words that are normally classified as nouns can be used as adjectives. So, too, can participles and pronouns when placed directly in front of a noun or pronoun. Personal pronouns used in this way are called **possessive adjectives.**
  EXAMPLES: brick walls (noun as adjective)
  blossoming flowers (participle as adjective)
  my hair (possessive adjective)

A. Underline the individual words that are acting as adjectives in the following sentences. Then underline each limiting adjective twice and circle each article.

1. The working paper on child poverty outlines the commission's main recommendations.
2. Student participation in extra-curricular activities has dropped for two reasons.
3. Some careless people left their knapsacks on the back stairs.
4. A strong wind blew in our faces as we trudged wearily up the long, steep incline.
5. Every time I turned away, that annoying cat would jump on my freshly made bed.

B. Write three adjectives to describe each noun.

1. bruise ______ ______ ______
2. worms ______ ______ ______
3. stranger ______ ______ ______
4. glass ______ ______ ______
5. box ______ ______ ______

C. Write sentences on the lines below. Use at least three adjectives in each sentence. Underline the adjectives.

1. ______
2. ______
3. ______
4. ______

Lesson 48 Comparing with Adjectives

- An adjective has three degrees of **comparison**: positive, comparative, and superlative.
- The simple form of the adjective is called the **positive degree**.
  EXAMPLE: Sinda is happy.
- Use the **comparative degree** to compare two people, groups, or things.
  EXAMPLES: Sinda is happier than Mariah.
  Paul is the older of the twins.
- Use the **superlative degree** to compare three or more people or things.
  EXAMPLE: Sinda is the happiest person on the block.
- For all adjectives of one syllable and a few adjectives of two syllables, add -er to form the comparative degree, and -est to form the superlative degree.
  EXAMPLES: high ⟶ higher ⟶ highest
- For some adjectives of two syllables and all adjectives of three or more syllables, use more or less to form the comparative and most or least to form the superlative.
  EXAMPLES: more/less painful ⟶ most/least painful

A. Write the comparative and superlative forms of each adjective.

Positive	Comparative	Superlative
1. expensive	______________	______________
2. rough	______________	______________
3. loud	______________	______________
4. stormy	______________	______________
5. scrawny	______________	______________

B. Complete each sentence with the correct degree of comparison of the adjective given in parentheses. Some of the forms are irregular.

1. (difficult) Of all my subjects at school, I would say physics is the ______________.
2. (good) Which is the ______________ university: UBC or Simon Fraser?
3. (little) I am making ______________ money at this job than I did last year.
4. (bad) This is the ______________ seafood chowder I've ever had!
5. (faithful) Fido is the ______________ dog I've ever owned.
6. (polite) Kieran is the ______________ of the two brothers.
7. (funny) Sophie has the ______________ of the two main roles in the play.
8. (responsible) Is Tina the ______________ of the two girls?
9. (efficient) There are many ways to get to Vancouver, but flying is the ______________.
10. (hopeful) Who is ______________ of winning: Carl or Simone?

Lesson 49 Adverbs

- **Adverbs** modify a verb, an adjective, or another adverb. They tell how, when, where, to what extent, or how often.

  EXAMPLES: Mr. Gupta arrived yesterday. (modifies the verb arrived)
  The street was particularly quiet. (modifies the adjective quiet)
  He smiled so broadly. (modifies the adverb broadly)

- Adverbs can also modify a whole sentence.

  EXAMPLE: Fortunately, not one person was injured in the crash.
  Significantly, the suspect made a large bank withdrawal the previous day.

- Many (but not all) adverbs end in -ly.

A. Underline each adverb. Indicate whether the adverb is modifying a verb, an adjective, another adverb, or the whole sentence.

1. We wish to speak privately. ____________
2. The sky glowered ominously as a few light raindrops fell earthward. ____________
3. An absurdly large cockroach scuttled by. ____________
4. First, knead the dough until it is very thin. ____________
5. He believes passionately that democratically elected governments must be protected. ____________
6. Mary Pratt's paintings often fetch quite startlingly high prices. ____________
7. Fortunately, he quickly devised a plan. ____________
8. Moreover, we have tentatively planned a reception at a very fancy inn. ____________
9. We will leave Thursday and will be away indefinitely. ____________
10. Melissa finally agreed because Jens looked so very sad! ____________

B. Write three adverbs that could be used to modify each verb.

1. travel ____________ ____________ ____________
2. whisper ____________ ____________ ____________
3. scream ____________ ____________ ____________
4. devour ____________ ____________ ____________
5. panic ____________ ____________ ____________
6. plan ____________ ____________ ____________
7. mimic ____________ ____________ ____________
8. spread ____________ ____________ ____________
9. confuse ____________ ____________ ____________
10. spray ____________ ____________ ____________

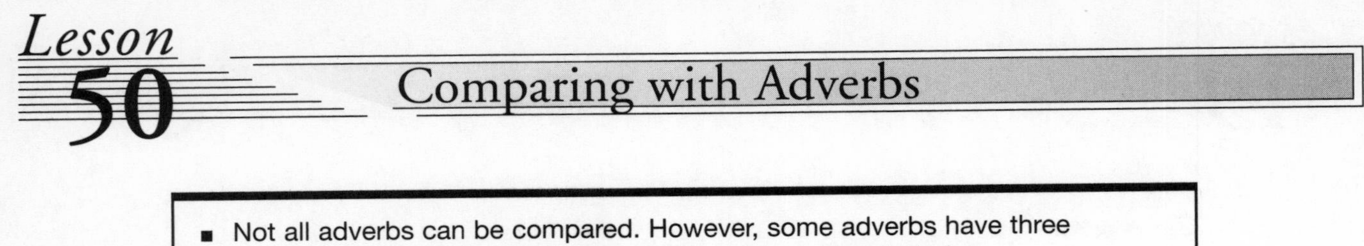

- Not all adverbs can be compared. However, some adverbs have three degrees of comparison: positive, comparative, and superlative.
- Use more (or less) to form the **comparative** and most (or least) to form the **superlative** of most adverbs, especially those that end in -ly.
  EXAMPLE: quickly ⟶ more quickly ⟶ most quickly
- Use -er to form the comparative degree and -est to form the superlative degree of most one-syllable and some two-syllable adverbs.
  EXAMPLE: soon ⟶ sooner ⟶ soonest

A. Write the comparative and superlative of each adverb.

Positive	Comparative	Superlative
1. directly	____________	____________
2. early	____________	____________
3. late	____________	____________
4. carefully	____________	____________
5. near	____________	____________
6. fast	____________	____________

B. Complete each sentence using the correct degree of comparison for each adverb in parentheses. Some of the forms are irregular.

1. (well) Samin did ____________ than I did on the music exam.
2. (badly) Of all the survivors, Franc was injured the ____________.
3. (greedily) Who devoured her meal ____________: Tamara or Ashley?
4. (kindly) The player was nice to everyone, but he spoke ____________ to a small child who was waiting patiently.
5. (wisely) Charles acted ____________ than the others.
6. (hard) We could have hired Justin or Milosz, but we felt that Justin would work ____________.
7. (deeply) Of all her suitors, Ophelia loved Hamlet ____________.
8. (long) If a hare, a tortoise, and a snail had a race, which of the three would take ____________ to reach the finish line?
9. (frankly) We can speak ____________ when we are alone than when we are with him.
10. (slowly) You walk ____________ than anyone else I know!

Lesson 51

Prepositions

- A **preposition** is a word that shows the relationship of a noun or a pronoun, called the **object of the preposition**, to another word in the sentence.

  EXAMPLE: He squeezed **under** the gate. (preposition: under; object of preposition: the gate)

- Some commonly used prepositions are listed below:

about	beside	of
above	between	over
across	by	through
against	for	to
among	from	toward
around	in	under
at	into	upon
behind	near	with

A. Underline each preposition and circle the object of the preposition.

1. Kiko sat in the seat behind the driver on the Greyhound bus to Calgary.
2. The apple above my head was almost within reach.
3. During both world wars, Canadian troops gained a reputation for courage and discipline.
4. Some prisoners of war tunnelled underneath the barriers to freedom.
5. The generation born in the 1980s and 1990s is very comfortable with the new technology.

- Use between when speaking of two people or things; use among when speaking of more than two.

  EXAMPLES: Divide the money between the two siblings.
  Divide the money among all three siblings.

- Use different from in most instances. Use different than only to avoid awkward phrasing, especially when followed by a clause.

  EXAMPLES: City life is different from country life.
  Awkward: Teenagers today are not much different from the way they were in the past.
  Better: Teenagers today are not much different than they were in the past.

B. Underline the correct preposition given in parentheses.

1. I walked down an alley (between, among) two buildings.
2. The four officers decided (between, among) themselves which one of them would take the first watch.
3. I look very (different from, different than) everyone else in my family.
4. The architecture in Montréal is (different from, different than) that of any other city in Canada.
5. The position of the government during an election campaign should be no (different from, different than) during its term in office.

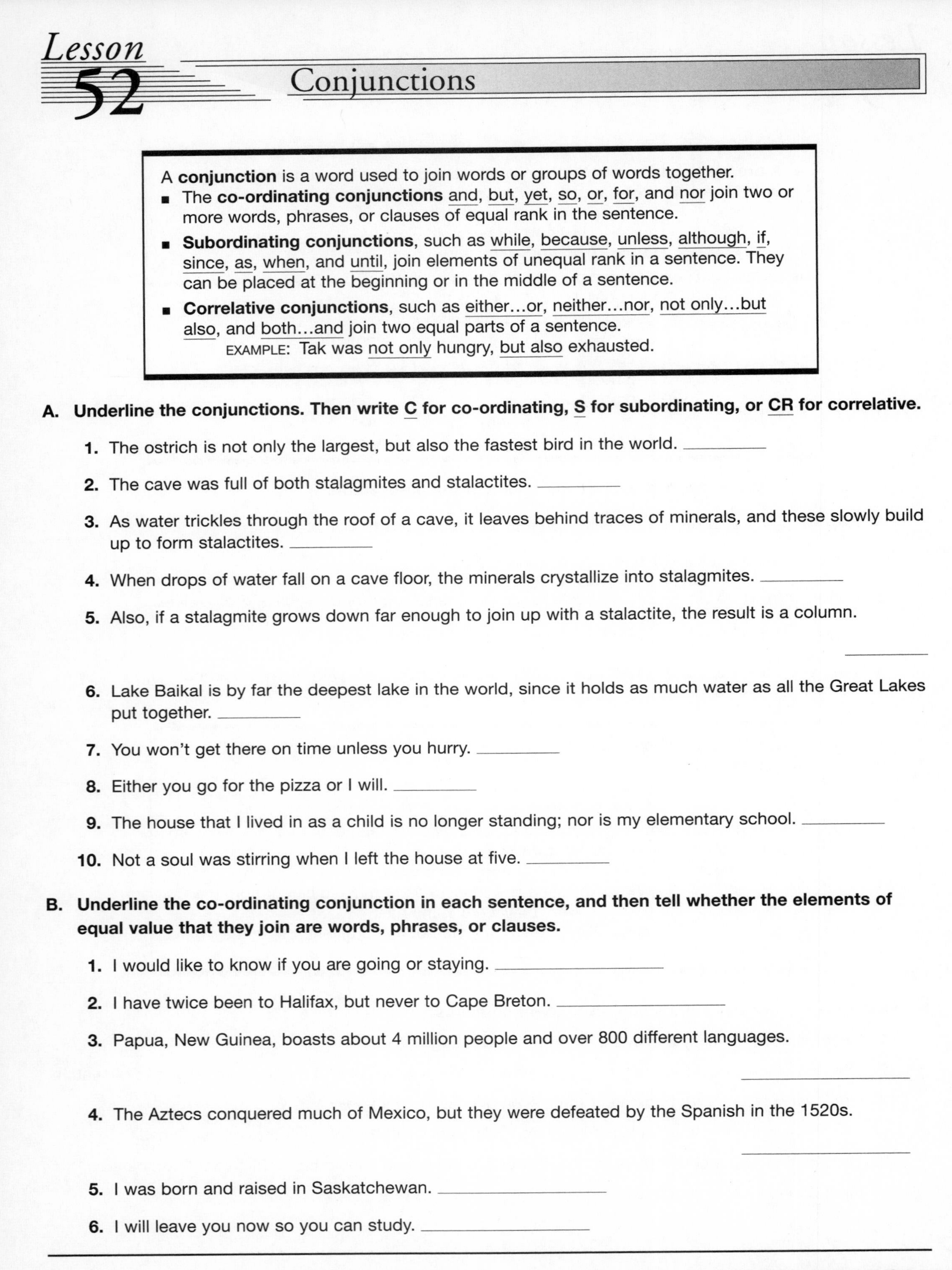

Lesson 52 Conjunctions

A **conjunction** is a word used to join words or groups of words together.

- The **co-ordinating conjunctions** and, but, yet, so, or, for, and nor join two or more words, phrases, or clauses of equal rank in the sentence.
- **Subordinating conjunctions**, such as while, because, unless, although, if, since, as, when, and until, join elements of unequal rank in a sentence. They can be placed at the beginning or in the middle of a sentence.
- **Correlative conjunctions**, such as either…or, neither…nor, not only…but also, and both…and join two equal parts of a sentence.
  EXAMPLE: Tak was not only hungry, but also exhausted.

A. Underline the conjunctions. Then write C for co-ordinating, S for subordinating, or CR for correlative.

1. The ostrich is not only the largest, but also the fastest bird in the world. ________
2. The cave was full of both stalagmites and stalactites. ________
3. As water trickles through the roof of a cave, it leaves behind traces of minerals, and these slowly build up to form stalactites. ________
4. When drops of water fall on a cave floor, the minerals crystallize into stalagmites. ________
5. Also, if a stalagmite grows down far enough to join up with a stalactite, the result is a column. ________
6. Lake Baikal is by far the deepest lake in the world, since it holds as much water as all the Great Lakes put together. ________
7. You won't get there on time unless you hurry. ________
8. Either you go for the pizza or I will. ________
9. The house that I lived in as a child is no longer standing; nor is my elementary school. ________
10. Not a soul was stirring when I left the house at five. ________

B. Underline the co-ordinating conjunction in each sentence, and then tell whether the elements of equal value that they join are words, phrases, or clauses.

1. I would like to know if you are going or staying. ________________
2. I have twice been to Halifax, but never to Cape Breton. ________________
3. Papua, New Guinea, boasts about 4 million people and over 800 different languages. ________________
4. The Aztecs conquered much of Mexico, but they were defeated by the Spanish in the 1520s. ________________
5. I was born and raised in Saskatchewan. ________________
6. I will leave you now so you can study. ________________

Double Negatives

- A **double negative** occurs when there are two negative words in a sentence. The two negatives cancel themselves out and make a positive.

  EXAMPLE: **Double negative:** You are not going nowhere.
  Negative: You are going nowhere.
  Negative: You are not going anywhere.

Rewrite each sentence in two different ways, eliminating the double negative.

1. I wouldn't never be caught in public wearing some of those designer fashions! ____________________

   ____

2. I can't hardly hear a thing over all that racket! ____________________

   ____

3. Don't those cookies have no sugar in them? ____________________

   ____

4. There isn't nobody around to explain what is happening. ____________________

   ____

5. You can't scarcely expect to travel from Moncton to Victoria in four days. ____________________

   ____

6. Isn't none of that delicious stew left? ____________________

   ____

7. Victor doesn't never travel without his camera. ____________________

   ____

8. I can't barely see the stage from here. ____________________

   ____

9. Paola says she didn't notice nothing wrong with the car. ____________________

   ____

10. I can't let no one in right now. ____________________

    ____

Lesson 54 Prepositional Phrases

Phrases can act as nouns, adjectives, or adverbs in a sentence.

- A **prepositional phrase** is a group of words that begins with a preposition and ends with a noun or pronoun.

  EXAMPLE: in the ground   over the top   by New Year's   except me

- Prepositional phrases usually act as adjectives or adverbs in a sentence.

  EXAMPLES: **Adjective:** The **woman** (antecedent) with red hair (prep. phrase) is the senior resident.

  Adverb: Maria **ran** (antecedent) to the store (prep. phrase).

A. Put parentheses around each prepositional phrase, and underline the preposition. Then indicate whether the phrase functions as an adjective or an adverb in the sentence.

1. Justine divides her time between Montréal and Toronto. ____________
2. Remy and I spent the day in the mall. ____________
3. The ticket for the train expires next January. ____________
4. This collection of Alice Munro short stories is her best yet. ____________
5. I fell asleep before *The National*. ____________
6. Everyone except Diane began right away. ____________
7. The fundraising target this month was reached by May 15. ____________
8. This is without a doubt the best soup I have ever had. ____________
9. The woman who had so many packages fell off her seat. ____________
10. Gasping, Finn leaned against the wall. ____________

B. For each preposition below, write a sentence using the preposition in a phrase that functions as an adjective. Then write another sentence for each preposition, this time using it in a phrase that functions as an adverb.

1. above ____________
2. beyond ____________
3. during ____________
4. around ____________
5. before ____________

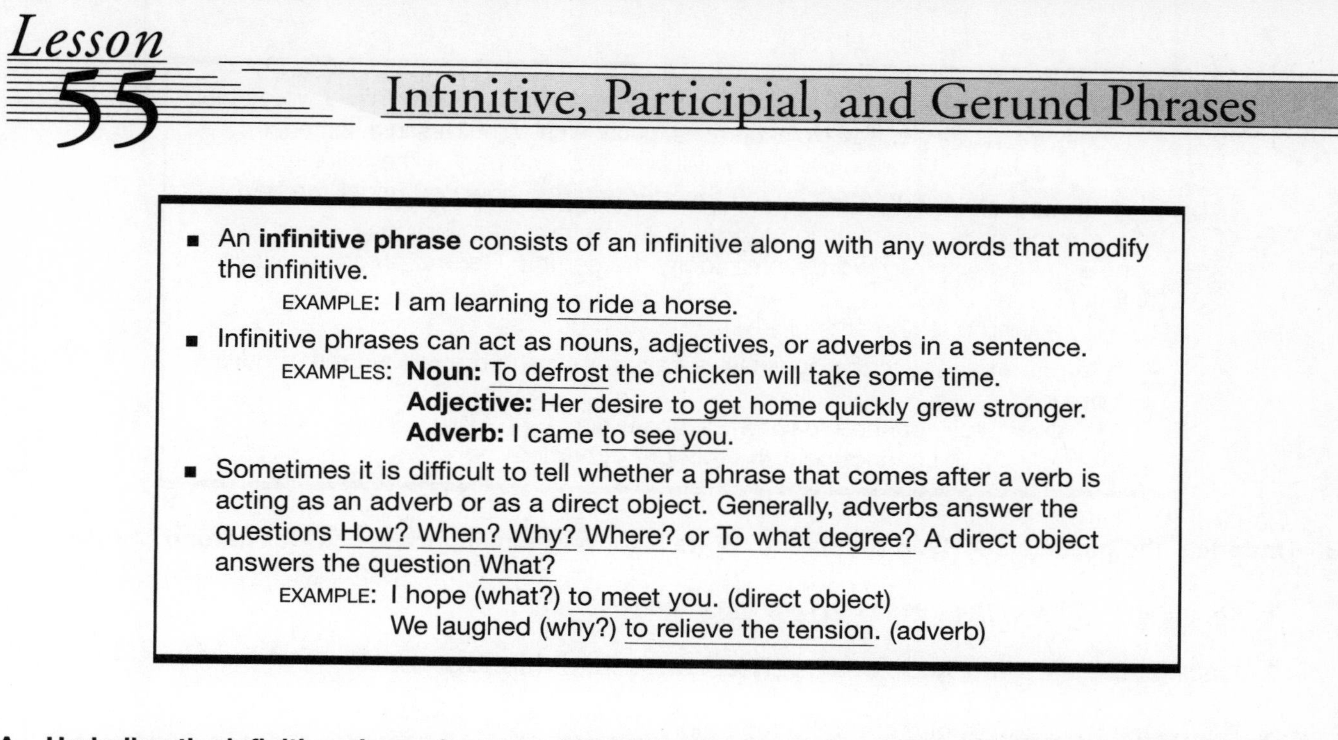

Lesson 55 Infinitive, Participial, and Gerund Phrases

- An **infinitive phrase** consists of an infinitive along with any words that modify the infinitive.

  EXAMPLE: I am learning to ride a horse.

- Infinitive phrases can act as nouns, adjectives, or adverbs in a sentence.

  EXAMPLES: **Noun:** To defrost the chicken will take some time.
  Adjective: Her desire to get home quickly grew stronger.
  Adverb: I came to see you.

- Sometimes it is difficult to tell whether a phrase that comes after a verb is acting as an adverb or as a direct object. Generally, adverbs answer the questions How? When? Why? Where? or To what degree? A direct object answers the question What?

  EXAMPLE: I hope (what?) to meet you. (direct object)
  We laughed (why?) to relieve the tension. (adverb)

A. Underline the infinitive phrase in each of the following sentences. Indicate whether it functions as a noun, adjective, or adverb.

1. To call collect sometimes requires the operator's assistance. ____________
2. To celebrate your birthday, I baked a cake. ____________
3. I hope to run into them at the flea market on Saturday. ____________
4. To counteract the effects of the poison requires a special serum. ____________
5. Dileeni's strong desire to reach Whitehorse by Thursday kept her going. ____________
6. To win the race, she ran faster than she ever had before. ____________
7. To make great soufflé requires patience and practice. ____________
8. The person to speak with is away from her desk right now. ____________
9. Russell knows a great way to catch bats. ____________
10. To pay for that CD player, I will work all summer as a lifeguard. ____________
11. I was surprised to find you awake so early. ____________
12. Machiko prefers to travel alone. ____________
13. If you feel the need to cough, please cover your mouth. ____________
14. This lesson is difficult to understand. ____________
15. To leave now seems rude. ____________
16. Whoever takes over that job will be expected to fill some big shoes. ____________

- **Participial phrases** contain a present or past participle along with any words that modify the participle. Participial phrases function as adjectives in a sentence.
  EXAMPLES: Taking careful aim, Michael shot the dart at the bull's-eye.
  Frightened by the thunder, my dog cowered under the bed.
- A **gerund phrase** contains a gerund (the -ing form of a verb when used as a noun) along with any words that modify the gerund. Gerund phrases always function as nouns.
  EXAMPLE: Taking careful aim is crucial in darts.
- In formal writing, use the possessive case for a noun or pronoun that modifies a gerund.
  EXAMPLES: Joanne's leaving will upset him.
  I cannot bear the thought of her leaving.

B. Underline the participial or gerund phrase. Write P for participial phrase or G for gerund phrase.

1. One of the duties of the treasurer is signing cheques. ________
2. Making the most of the good weather, Heath decided to walk to school. ________
3. Pulling the fire alarm turned out to be a bad idea. ________
4. Scraped and bruised, Connor picked himself up from under his bike. ________
5. Excusing herself from the table, Rula went to answer the door. ________
6. Wearing a hat is a good idea. ________
7. Surviving an arctic winter is quite an accomplishment. ________
8. Held up for days by bad weather, the travellers were happy to make it home. ________
9. My least favourite job is washing the dishes. ________
10. I worked all day in the garden, ignoring the rain. ________

C. Write one sentence that contains a participial phrase, and one sentence that contains a gerund phrase.

Participial phrase ____

____

Gerund phrase ____

____

D. Fill in the blank with the correct form of the noun or pronoun in parentheses.

1. Veronica loved the idea of (we) ________________ making supper.
2. With the (storm) ________________ passing we finally were able to start our trip.
3. (Pat) ________________ crying has nothing to do with us.
4. (You) ________________ singing might have disturbed the baby

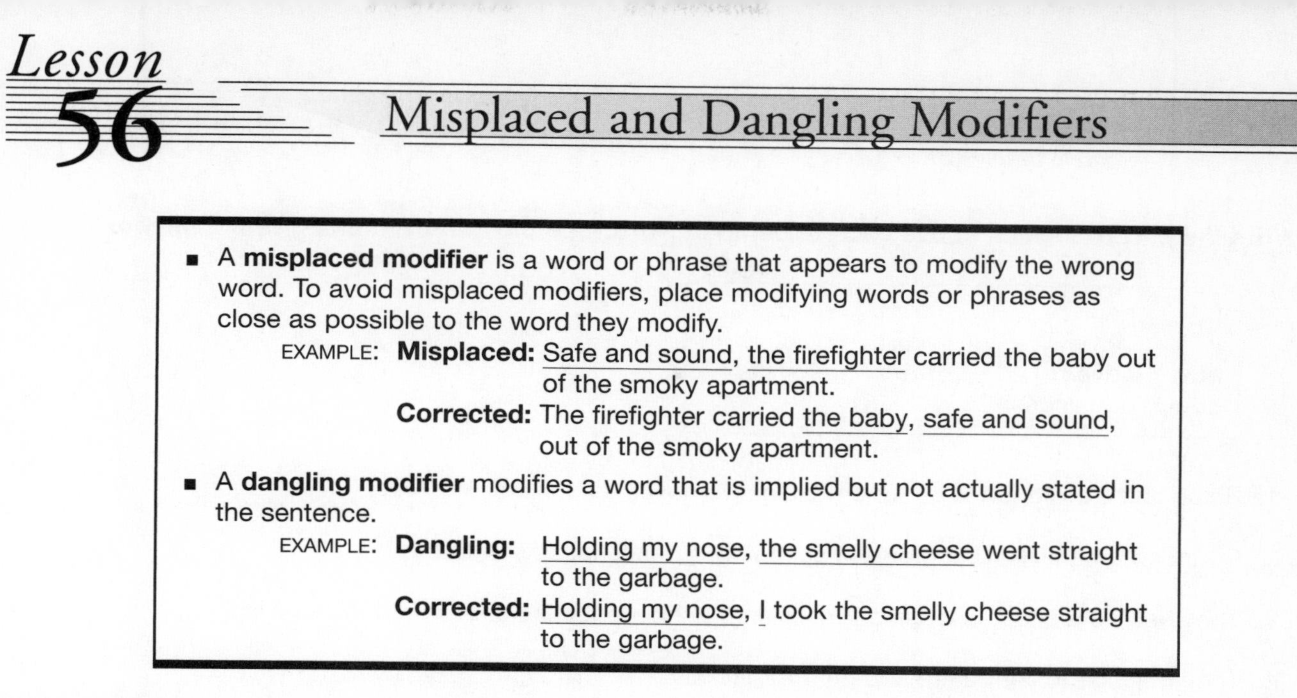

Lesson 56 Misplaced and Dangling Modifiers

- A **misplaced modifier** is a word or phrase that appears to modify the wrong word. To avoid misplaced modifiers, place modifying words or phrases as close as possible to the word they modify.

  EXAMPLE: **Misplaced:** Safe and sound, the firefighter carried the baby out of the smoky apartment.

  Corrected: The firefighter carried the baby, safe and sound, out of the smoky apartment.

- A **dangling modifier** modifies a word that is implied but not actually stated in the sentence.

  EXAMPLE: **Dangling:** Holding my nose, the smelly cheese went straight to the garbage.

  Corrected: Holding my nose, I took the smelly cheese straight to the garbage.

Rewrite the following sentences to eliminate misplaced or dangling modifiers.

1. Screaming and waving, the roller coaster dropped us to the ground.

   ____

2. Parvati visited the cottage where Stephen Leacock lived during the 1930s last summer.

   ____

3. The house was empty during the winter without you.

   ____

4. Gleaming with a new coat of paint, the mechanic brought me my car.

   ____

5. The mouse ran to escape the cat down the hole.

   ____

6. Working round the clock, the project was finished on schedule.

   ____

7. Waiting patiently at the baggage carousel in Winnipeg, my bags had been rerouted to St. John's.

   ____

8. Looking for gold, the Caribou Wagon Road was travelled by over 100 000 people in the late 1800s.

   ____

9. Talking to Jiang, the phone cord got pulled out of the wall.

   ____

10. Dave was sitting by the fire when I came in to warm his feet.

   ____

Review

A. Write the part of speech above each underlined word. Use the abbreviations given in the box.

n.	noun	**pron.**	pronoun
v.	verb	**adj.**	adjective
adv.	adverb	**prep.**	preposition
conj.	conjunction		

1. Ralph is the protagonist of William Golding's novel *The Lord of the Flies*.
2. Stranded on an island, a group of schoolboys descends into anarchy.
3. They believe a beast is loose on the island, although it is actually within themselves.
4. They manage to light a fire and hunt for food.
5. The conch shell that the boys use initially to call one another could be a symbol of authority.

B. Write the correct form of the noun in parentheses.

1. Riswan spoke to the (party) ______________ host.
2. Between us we ate six hamburgers and drank seven (milkshake) ______________.
3. That book rates all the university (campus) ______________ in Canada.
4. The first page of the violin (concerto) ______________ score is missing.
5. The (Stokowski) ______________ niece won an athletic scholarship.

C. Write the verb form that corresponds with the instructions.

1. Present participle of **give** ______________
2. Present progressive of **guess**: I ______________
3. Past progressive of **see**: He ______________
4. Past, passive voice of **refuse**: We ______________
5. Future tense of **describe**: They ______________
6. Future perfect, passive voice of **know**: You ______________
7. Past progressive, passive voice of **receive**: It ______________
8. Past of **set**: I ______________
9. Future perfect of **lay**: They ______________
10. Past progressive of **lie**: She ______________

D. Underline the form of the verb that agrees with the subject.

1. The players on the softball team (is, are) meeting for a practice on Thursday.
2. Some of the pizza slices, but not every one, (has, have) pepperoni.
3. The dogs and their energetic owner (was, were) out for a romp in the park.
4. Michael, or maybe his twin, often (walk, walks) past the library where I work.
5. Either my keys or my wallet always (seem, seems) to go missing just as I am leaving.

E. For each underlined phrase, circle the preposition, participle, infinitive, or gerund. Then write ADJ, ADV, or N above each phrase to indicate its function.

1. Species are disappearing rapidly from our planet.
2. Formed in 1961, the World Wildlife Fund works to save animals on the endangered list.
3. Slowing down the rate of extinction is difficult unless governments can help to support these efforts.
4. Some countries with endangered species are unwilling to make changes, however.
5. Saving endangered species sometimes has consequences for the economy, which can discourage governments from acting.

F. Underline the pronoun in parentheses that agrees with the antecedent. Circle the antecedent.

1. René Lévesque and Lucien Bouchard both believed that (his, their) province, Québec, should separate from the rest of Canada.
2. Everybody should study the history of (his or her, their) own country.
3. Selena and James will be visiting (his, he and she) aunt in Vermillion, BC, next week.
4. I bought (me, myself) a sundae as a reward for losing five kilograms.
5. The owners of that horse, (who, whom) also own several racehorses, are excellent trainers.

G. Underline the correct adjective or adverb from the pair given in parentheses.

1. Amber planned the party (real, really) carefully.
2. Which of these two chocolate bars is (more, most) delicious?
3. It looks to me as if Bjorn is the (taller, tallest) in the class.
4. Fighter plane pilots were (less likelier, less likely) to survive World War I than most other military personnel.
5. I felt (more badly, worse) about lying to you than about damaging your car.

Using What You've Learned

A. Read the following passage and answer the questions below.

In the late 1960s, most of the music heard on Canadian radio stations was imported from the United States or Britain. Canadian music was often scorned. All that changed in 1971 when Pierre Juneau, the minister of communications, introduced Canadian content regulations. Radio stations were required to play at least 25 percent Canadian content during prime listening periods. Many owners of radio stations were upset about these regulations, which they claimed would drive away their audience.

Since that time, however, Canadian music has blossomed. Hearing Canadian music and Canadian artists on the radio is no longer unusual. Popular singers such as Alanis Morissette, Bryan Adams, and Celine Dion have become international celebrities and have put Canada on the map. Many observers believe that the Canadian content regulations played a large part in this success. Some have suggested that similar rules should apply to the contents of magazines, hoping for an increase in Canadian content there, too.

1. Find seven proper nouns. ________ ________ ________

   ________ ________ ________ ________

2. Find a collective noun. ________

3. Find three passive verbs. ________ ________ ________

4. Find a present perfect verb. ________

5. Find a participial phrase that begins with a present participle. ________

   ____

6. Find a gerund phrase. ________

7. Find an infinitive phrase. ________

8. Find a relative clause. ________

9. Find two indefinite pronouns used as the subjects of sentences. ________

   ____

10. Find a participial phrase that begins with a past participle. ________

    ____

11. Find four prepositional phrases in the first sentence. Tell whether each is acting as an adjective or adverb in the sentence.

    ____

    ____

    ____

    ____

B. Read the following paragraphs. Then rewrite them, correcting any errors in the following:

- **subject–verb agreement**
- **pronoun–antecedent agreement**
- **verb tense**
- **verb usage (may/can; teach/learn)**
- **comparative adjectives or adverbs**
- **the use of double negatives**
- **misplaced or dangling modifiers**
- **the use of nouns or pronouns to modify a gerund**

When we turn on the tap, we expect an abundant supply of clean, fresh water to flow out. Having one of the world's largest supplies of fresh water, these expectations may usually be met in Canada. However, in many other countries, water is a scarce commodity. Useless for drinking or agricultural needs unless the salt is removed, the world contains much less fresh water (2.5 percent) than it does salt water (97.5 percent). The United Nations say that in 25 years, two-thirds of the world can be experiencing water shortages.

The first time most Canadians really started to think about the safety of its water supply was in 2000, when seven people in Walkerton, Ontario, died from drinking tainted tap water. Thousands more was taken ill. All of a sudden, we begun to realize how crucial a safe, clean supply of water was. But we will all have to pay more close attention to the way we use water in the future. For example, learning people to use a glass of water to brush his or her teeth, instead of letting the tap run, would save 14 litres of water per person every time.

Canadians are the second larger consumers of water in the world. The average Canadian uses 326 litre's of water a day for baths, showers, toilet flushing, drinking, laundry, and lawn watering. In France, the average is only 150 litres a day, and most developing country's has considerably lower consumption rates.

Of course, every bit helps, but us cutting down on domestic consumption won't never be enough on it's own to preserve the water supply. Industry and agriculture is by far the biggest users of water. The computer industry alone use 1.5 trillion litre's a year, and produce 300 billion litre's of waste water. Even though the world population have only doubled, water demand has grown sevenfold in the last century. New way's will have to be found to regulate water use by industry and agriculture.

Lesson 57 Using Capital Letters

Capitalize

- the word <u>I</u>, the first word of a sentence, and often the first word of each line of poetry
- all important words in the titles of books, poems, stories, and songs (*The Stone Angel; The Collected Works of Billy the Kid*)
- all proper nouns and proper adjectives (a proper adjective is an adjective that is made from a proper noun; for example, <u>Canadian</u>)
- family relationships when used as names ("I will ask <u>Dad</u>." BUT "I will ask my dad.")
- a person's title when it comes before a name (<u>Doctor</u> Biddiscombe)
- the first letter in titles, days and months, and parts of addresses, or their abbreviations (Ms.; Mon.; Sept.; Blvd.)
- all letters in the abbreviations of provinces (NF, ON, AB)
- the first word of the salutation and closing of a letter (<u>Dear</u> sir; <u>Yours</u> truly)
- all geographic place names (Vancouver, Charlottetown; the Rockies; Lake Ontario)
- directions ONLY when used to designate a specific region or when part of a place name (the North; the West Coast; South Asia). Otherwise, directions are lower-case. (We drove east.)

A. Correct any errors in capitalization in the following sentences. Underline each letter that should be capitalized.

1. for lunch on sunday we had french stick, cheese, and cold potato soup.
2. my uncle, pierre laflamme, read us a poem titled "the bull calf," by the canadian poet irving layton.
3. our captain saw private kayla vanclieff on *who wants to be a millionaire*, *canadian edition*.
4. I saw a movie about the life of dr. norman bethune, a canadian who became a hero in china.
5. please send the package to 255 riel blvd., harvest gate, mb p3j 4h2.
6. the planet mercury is the closest planet to the sun, according to my astronomy book.
7. My friends on the east coast know how dangerous it can be in the north atlantic.
8. st. catherine street is a few blocks south of sherbrooke street in montréal.
9. kate and anna mcgarrigle wrote a song called "heart like a wheel."
10. learning mandarin will help you to understand cantonese, vietnamese, japanese, and many other languages of south asia.
11. in september, we will be moving north to gimli, manitoba, which has a large finnish population.
12. i love to eat thai food, but it is too spicy for my mother!

- Capitalize the first word of a direct quotation if it is used as a complete sentence or if it is a complete sentence in the original.

  EXAMPLES: A spokesperson for Reckitt and Runne stated: "We are committed to doing whatever is necessary to remedy the situation."

  A spokesperson for Reckitt and Runne stated that the company was "committed to doing whatever is necessary to remedy the situation."

B. Read the following original statement. Then, in your notebook, correct any errors in capitalization in the examples that follow. If there are no errors, write C.

Original Statement:

"Skateboarders have been without a place to practise their sport for several years now. The passage of a municipal by-law prohibiting skateboarding in public places stops youth from engaging in a healthy physical activity, and provides one more incentive for young people to turn to other, possibly less wholesome, forms of entertainment. Other cities the same size as ours—and even smaller towns—have found the means to provide skateboard parks for their youth. Why can't we? It is useless to complain about skateboarders taking over city streets and public spaces if no one is willing to provide alternatives."

— Evan Levy, Youth for Skateboarding

1. Evan Levy, spokesperson for Youth for Skateboarding, claims that it is time the city provided adequate facilities for skateboarders, since "Other cities the same size as ours—and even smaller towns—have found the means to provide skateboard parks for their youth."
2. Levy believes that complaints about skateboarders on city streets are "Useless" unless city council decides to build a skateboard park.
3. According to Levy, "Skateboarders have been without a place to practise their sport for several years now."
4. Will the by-law provide "One more incentive," as Levy claims, "For young people to turn to other, possibly less wholesome, forms of entertainment"?
5. What are these "Smaller towns" with skateboarding facilities that Levy refers to?

- Writers, advertisers, and poets may break the rules of capitalization for a specific purpose or to create a particular mood or impression.

C. Find a poem in an anthology or an advertisement in a magazine that breaks one or more rules of capitalization. Bring the selection to class and explain what rules have been broken. In small groups, choose one poem or advertisement and discuss why the writer might have chosen to write the piece in this way.

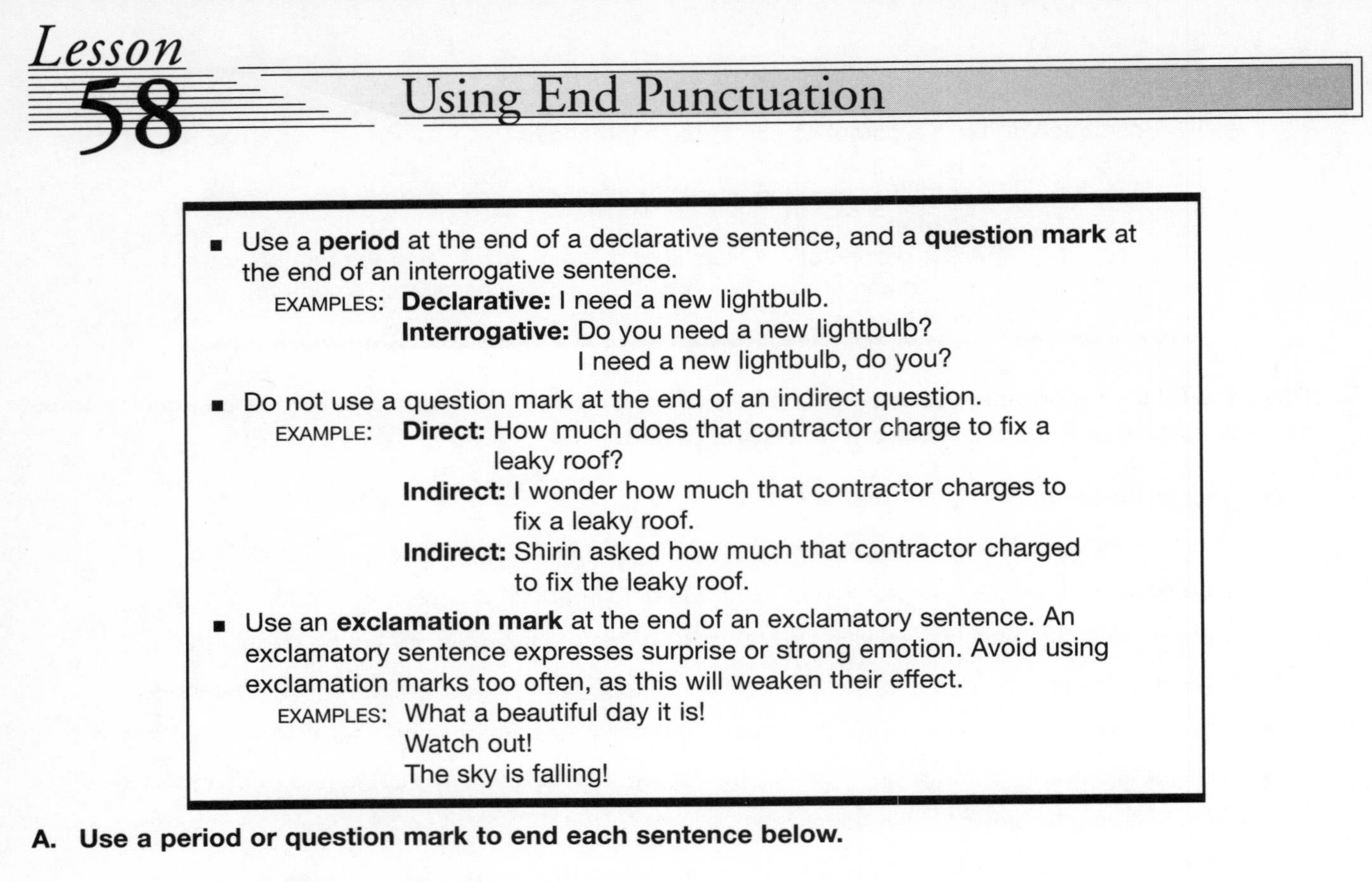

Lesson 58 Using End Punctuation

- Use a **period** at the end of a declarative sentence, and a **question mark** at the end of an interrogative sentence.
  EXAMPLES: **Declarative:** I need a new lightbulb.
  Interrogative: Do you need a new lightbulb?
  I need a new lightbulb, do you?
- Do not use a question mark at the end of an indirect question.
  EXAMPLE: **Direct:** How much does that contractor charge to fix a leaky roof?
  Indirect: I wonder how much that contractor charges to fix a leaky roof.
  Indirect: Shirin asked how much that contractor charged to fix the leaky roof.
- Use an **exclamation mark** at the end of an exclamatory sentence. An exclamatory sentence expresses surprise or strong emotion. Avoid using exclamation marks too often, as this will weaken their effect.
  EXAMPLES: What a beautiful day it is!
  Watch out!
  The sky is falling!

A. Use a period or question mark to end each sentence below.

1. You want me to bring what to school tomorrow ________
2. I'm amazed at how well the badminton team did, aren't you ________
3. It's uncanny how Ariel and Samantha resemble each other, if you ask me ________
4. Matthew asked that we refrain from talking during his performance ________
5. Wouldn't you love a chocolate bar right now ________
6. Please, could I take your picture ________
7. Your résumé is too long—or is that your autobiography ________
8. I asked, "Will you honour your guarantee in this case ________"
9. Please return to your seats ________
10. Do you honestly think anyone will believe such a crazy story ________

B. The following passage has too many exclamation marks. Underline those that you think should be changed, writing the correct punctuation above. Leave no more than two exclamation marks in the revised version.

On my way home from school, I slipped and fell head over heels on a patch of ice! As I was shaking my head to get over the shock, what do you think I saw! It was a $10 bill, right there on the sidewalk! Someone must have dropped it right where I had fallen! Suddenly my head didn't hurt nearly so much! I was rich! I stuffed it in my pocket and got up! I felt that my luck had changed! Then I remembered: I had had a $10 bill in my pocket this morning! The bill must be my own!

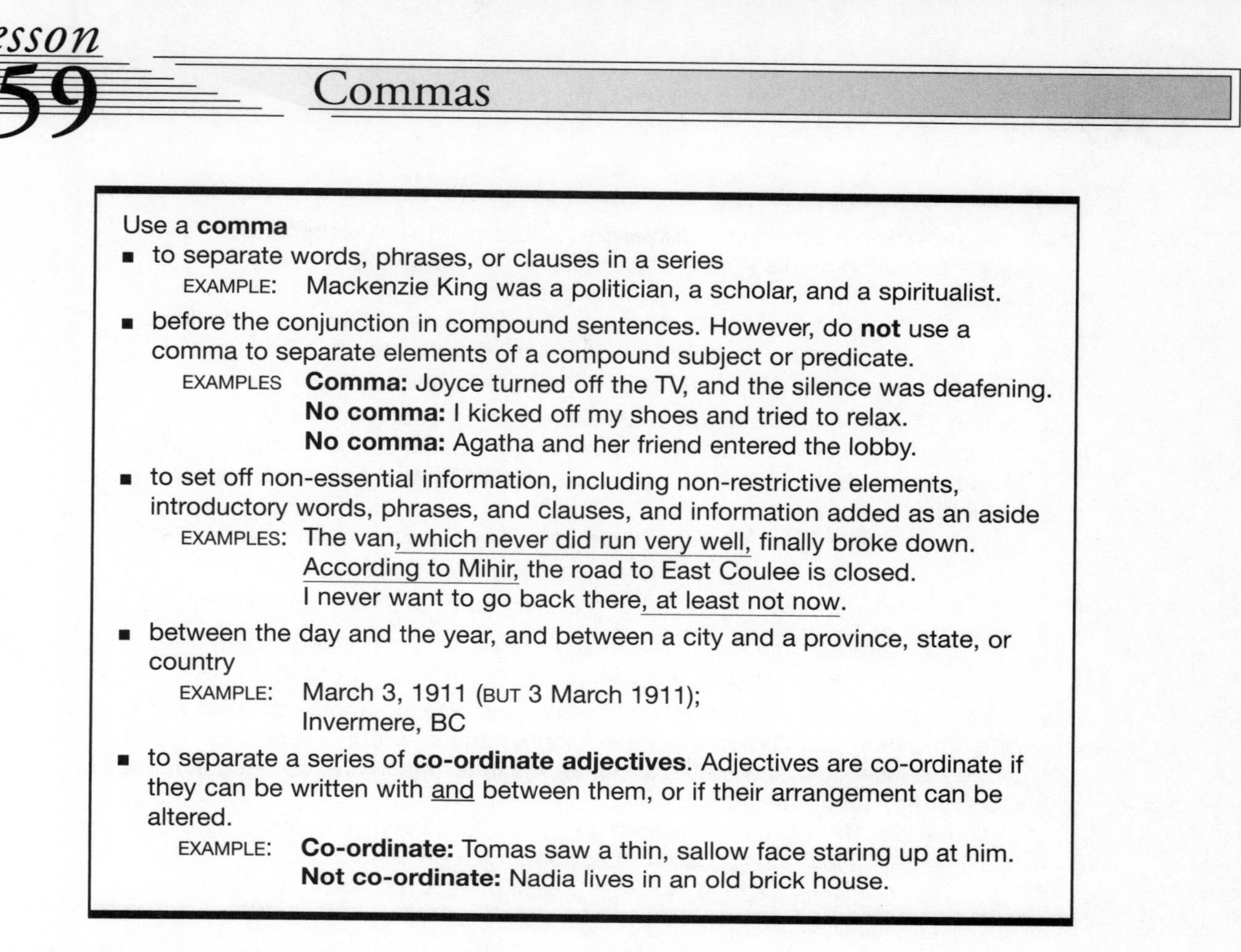

Lesson 59 Commas

Use a **comma**

- to separate words, phrases, or clauses in a series
  EXAMPLE: Mackenzie King was a politician, a scholar, and a spiritualist.
- before the conjunction in compound sentences. However, do **not** use a comma to separate elements of a compound subject or predicate.
  EXAMPLES **Comma:** Joyce turned off the TV, and the silence was deafening.
  No comma: I kicked off my shoes and tried to relax.
  No comma: Agatha and her friend entered the lobby.
- to set off non-essential information, including non-restrictive elements, introductory words, phrases, and clauses, and information added as an aside
  EXAMPLES: The van, which never did run very well, finally broke down.
  According to Mihir, the road to East Coulee is closed.
  I never want to go back there, at least not now.
- between the day and the year, and between a city and a province, state, or country
  EXAMPLE: March 3, 1911 (BUT 3 March 1911);
  Invermere, BC
- to separate a series of **co-ordinate adjectives**. Adjectives are co-ordinate if they can be written with and between them, or if their arrangement can be altered.
  EXAMPLE: **Co-ordinate:** Tomas saw a thin, sallow face staring up at him.
  Not co-ordinate: Nadia lives in an old brick house.

Correct these sentences by adding commas in the appropriate places.

1. My father was not only a great dad he was also an expert marksman a talented storyteller and an avid baseball fan.
2. According to most historians the incident that sparked World War I was the assassination of the Austrian Prince Franz Ferdinand on June 28 1914.
3. Julian Hannah and Maria who worked together on their project scored highest for their presentation.
4. With all due respect I don't like what you're telling me and I don't care to discuss it any further.
5. Whenever I visit Victoria Beach Manitoba memories of long blissful happy childhood summers come flooding back.
6. Heiko made a delicious cabbage salad Diana baked her special sesame chicken which was very tasty and Costa bought sweet warm honey-drenched baklava from the local Greek bakery.
7. When gathering information from a Web site consider the general reliability of the site and always try to verify the accuracy of the information from another source.
8. He was clever but couldn't make decisions at least not without a good deal of long hard thinking.
9. In the barn on my grandparents' farm the cows were making a great fuss perhaps because they had not been milked.
10. Selma whom everyone mistrusted at first proved to be a loyal trustworthy hard-working employee.
11. I gave Adrian my old bicycle which I never use any more.
12. If you want to stay healthy eat well and exercise regularly.

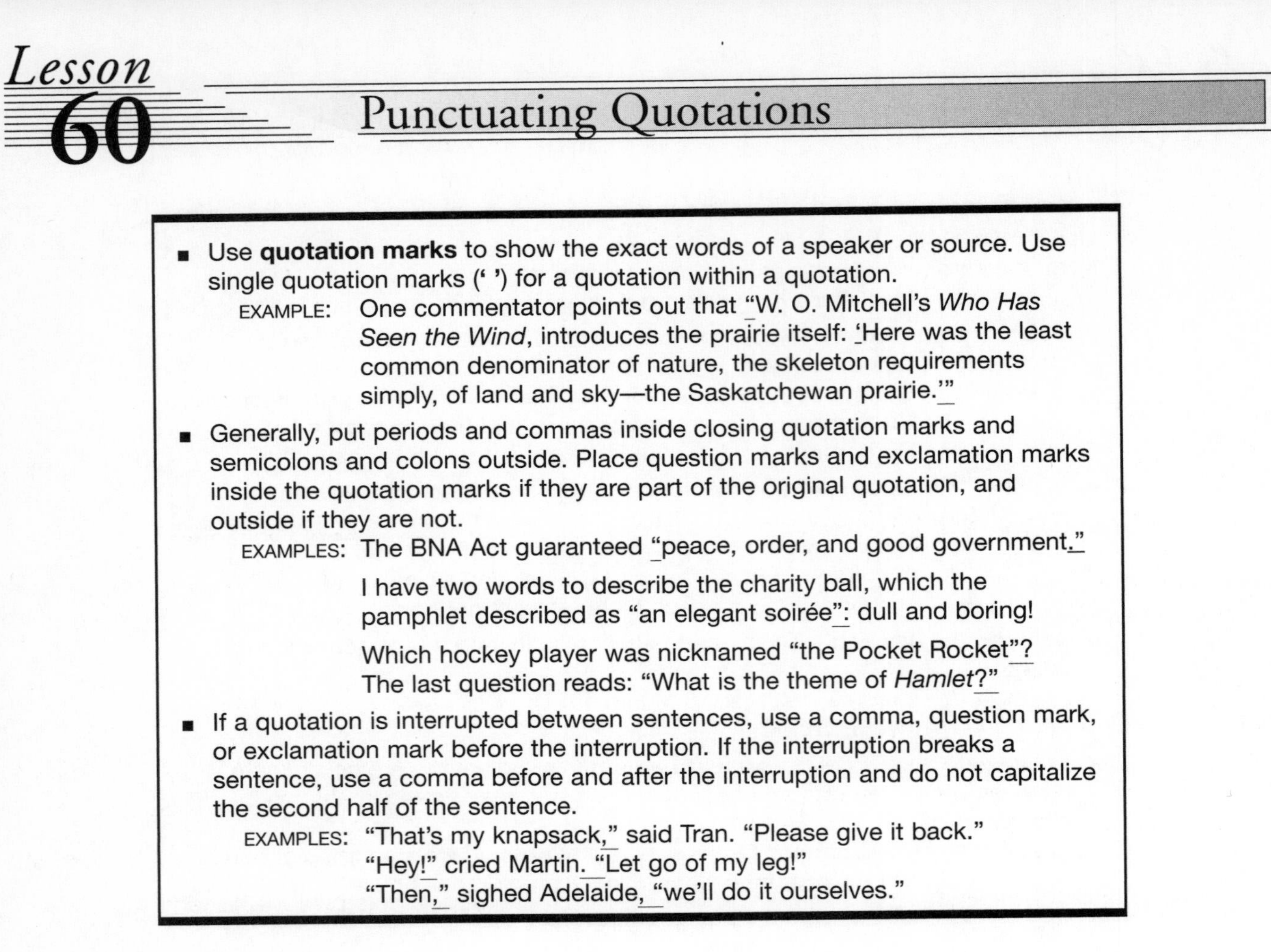

Lesson 60 Punctuating Quotations

- Use **quotation marks** to show the exact words of a speaker or source. Use single quotation marks (' ') for a quotation within a quotation.

  EXAMPLE: One commentator points out that "W. O. Mitchell's *Who Has Seen the Wind*, introduces the prairie itself: 'Here was the least common denominator of nature, the skeleton requirements simply, of land and sky—the Saskatchewan prairie.'"

- Generally, put periods and commas inside closing quotation marks and semicolons and colons outside. Place question marks and exclamation marks inside the quotation marks if they are part of the original quotation, and outside if they are not.

  EXAMPLES: The BNA Act guaranteed "peace, order, and good government."

  I have two words to describe the charity ball, which the pamphlet described as "an elegant soirée": dull and boring!

  Which hockey player was nicknamed "the Pocket Rocket"?
  The last question reads: "What is the theme of *Hamlet*?"

- If a quotation is interrupted between sentences, use a comma, question mark, or exclamation mark before the interruption. If the interruption breaks a sentence, use a comma before and after the interruption and do not capitalize the second half of the sentence.

  EXAMPLES: "That's my knapsack," said Tran. "Please give it back."
  "Hey!" cried Martin. "Let go of my leg!"
  "Then," sighed Adelaide, "we'll do it ourselves."

A. Rewrite the following quotations in your notebook, correcting any errors in punctuation.

1. "I believe, he cried, "In the future of this country and of its people"!
2. When did the Prime Minister tell the Cabinet that "the government's job is to be responsive to the needs of Canadian citizens?"
3. "Where do you get your crazy ideas," laughed Arden?
4. One leading expert in economic forecasting claims that "Canada's future depends on increasing our domestic productivity substantially in the next five years;" another believes that "freer trade with other countries is our best hope for a prosperous future."
5. One critic wrote, 'The soliloquy in Shakespeare's *Hamlet* that begins "To be or not to be" is perhaps the best-known English monologue of all time.'
6. "Hey, look," yelled Arnold! There's a hole in my pocket"!
7. Would you like it if someone called you a "difficult person to get to know?"
8. "My sister, he said, "Heard noises downstairs and called out Is anybody there?
9. Your letter addressed me as "Dear Mr. Ferenc;" however my name is Anna Fitzpatrick.
10. "I know you, she said, Don't you live next door to me"?
11. Who was it who said, "The bigger they are, the harder they fall?"

- Use **ellipses** (**...**) to indicate that material has been omitted from a quoted sentence. If the omission comes at the end of a sentence, a period follows the ellipses (**....**).
- Use **square brackets** (**[ ]**) when adding explanatory words that are not part of the original quotation. Also use square brackets if you have to change or replace a word in the original to make it fit in your sentence, or if you change a lower-case letter to a capital letter (or vice versa).

  EXAMPLE: "She [the finance minister] bought a charming pair of brogues." (explains to whom "she" refers)

  He felt that the budget "[did] not address the needs of the poor." (did replaces does in the original to make the sentence flow)

  "[S]omeone mentioned to him that this had long been a tradition for finance ministers...." (indicates change in capitalization)

B. Rewrite the following sentences in your notebook using ellipsis points to show that the underlined words have been omitted. Insert any words that are necessary in square brackets to make the meaning of the sentence clear.

1. Mary Arden was from a well-to-do family in Stratford. She married John Shakespeare, a glove-maker and farm commodities trader in 1557, and seven years later, in 1564, their eldest son, William, was born.
2. The first North American woman to reach the summit of Mount Everest was a Canadian: Sharon Wood, of Canmore, Alberta. Ms. Wood accomplished the feat on May 20, 1986, when she was just 28.
3. Learning how to fall properly is a skill that rollerbladers and skateboarders practise diligently. Skateboarders must learn to roll off the board in order to avoid hitting the pavement with a painful thud.

- For longer quotations (four lines or more), or poetry excerpts of more than two lines, do not use quotation marks. Instead, begin the quotation on a new line, and set it off from the text by indenting 10 spaces from the left margin. Include a sentence that introduces the quotation, followed by a colon.

  EXAMPLE: One writer explains the origin of a peculiar tradition in Canadian politics:

  > There is a tradition in Canadian Parliament that the finance minister must wear new shoes when he or she presents the budget. The first minister to do so was Mitchell Sharp in 1966–67. Sharp claims that someone mentioned to him that this had long been a tradition for finance ministers, and "I accepted that at face value and bought a good pair of shoes (Canadian made, $40) that I wore budget night."

C. In your notebook or on a computer, write a sentence to introduce the following quotation, and then write the quotation in the proper format for long quotations.

Original: "He was the greatest comic novelist in the English language since Charles Dickens. Like Dickens, Robertson Davies came to the novel with a theatrical background; possibly this gave him dramatic expectations. He expected the novel to perform for an audience—to be simultaneously entertaining and instructive; to be intellectually stimulating and emotionally cathartic."

(Source: John Irving, novelist, *Maclean's*, December 18, 1995)

Lesson 61 Quotation Marks, Italics, and Underlining

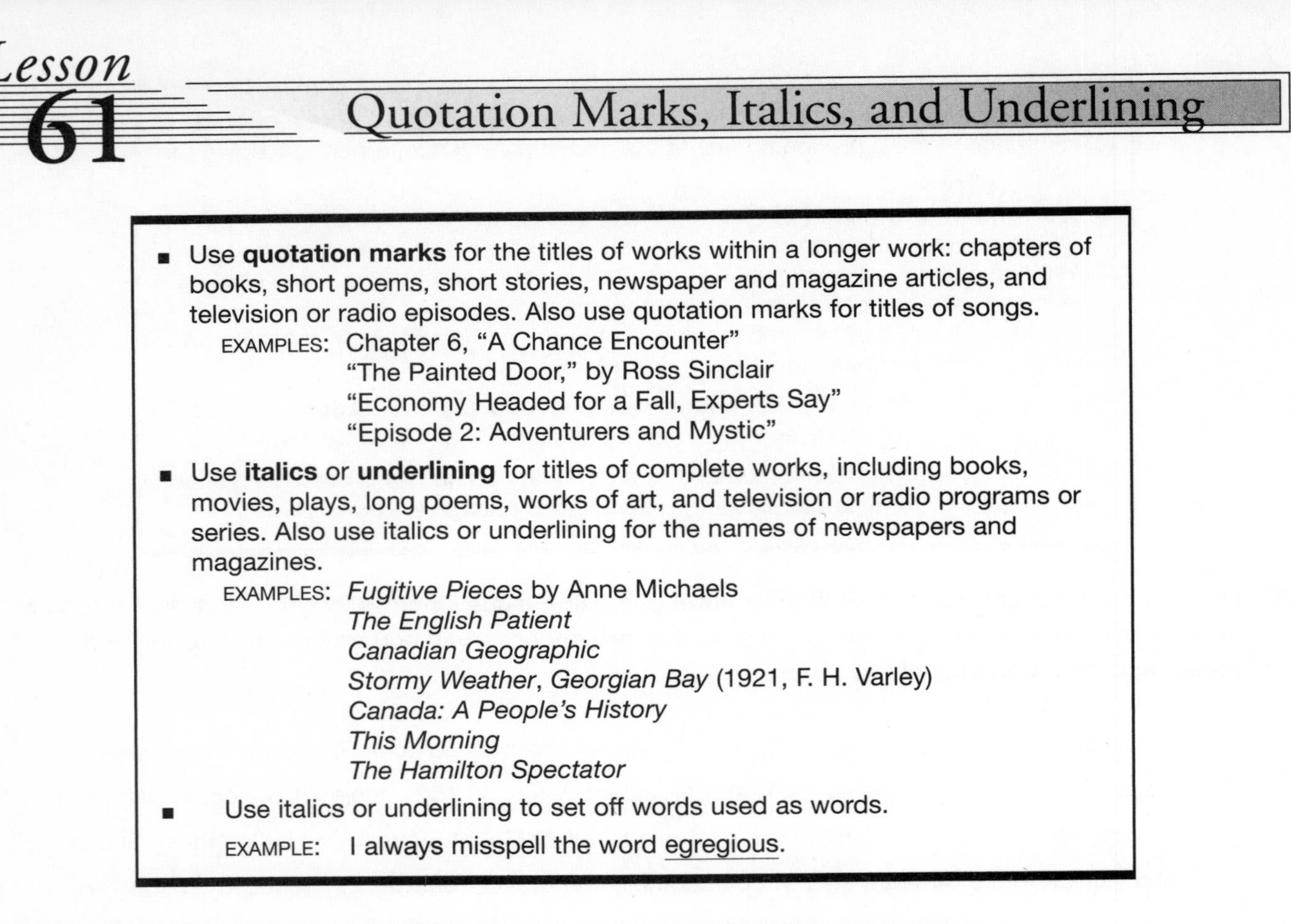

- Use **quotation marks** for the titles of works within a longer work: chapters of books, short poems, short stories, newspaper and magazine articles, and television or radio episodes. Also use quotation marks for titles of songs.

  EXAMPLES: Chapter 6, "A Chance Encounter"
  "The Painted Door," by Ross Sinclair
  "Economy Headed for a Fall, Experts Say"
  "Episode 2: Adventurers and Mystic"

- Use **italics** or **underlining** for titles of complete works, including books, movies, plays, long poems, works of art, and television or radio programs or series. Also use italics or underlining for the names of newspapers and magazines.

  EXAMPLES: *Fugitive Pieces* by Anne Michaels
  The English Patient
  Canadian Geographic
  Stormy Weather, *Georgian Bay* (1921, F. H. Varley)
  Canada: A People's History
  This Morning
  The Hamilton Spectator

- Use italics or underlining to set off words used as words.

  EXAMPLE: I always misspell the word egregious.

Add quotation marks and underlining where necessary in the following sentences.

1. The headline in The Globe and Mail this morning reads Government Slips in Polls.
2. The term cool is simply not an appropriate way to describe a science experiment.
3. Budge Wilson's short story The Dandelion Garden is in a collection of her stories that is also called The Dandelion Garden.
4. In the next episode of the show Teen Tigers, titled Aaron's Big Mistake, one of the characters falls for a con artist, who promises she will get him a career in modelling.
5. Michelangelo's most famous sculpture is called David.
6. Daphne Odjig's mural, titled The Indian in Transition, hangs in the foyer of the National Art Centre.
7. If you like science fiction, try a book titled The Other Place, by Monica Hughes.
8. This poem, The Fish, by Elizabeth Bishop, was included in the anthology The Rattle Bag, which was edited by Seamus Heaney and Ted Hughes.
9. I was watching Hockey Night in Canada, but my brother wanted to change the channel and watch MuchMusic instead.
10. We are supposed to read Chapter 5, Ecosystems in the Biology Basics text.
11. The word technology appears 15 times in chapter 1 of this book, titled The Future of Society.
12. The movie West Side Story is an updated version of Shakespeare's play Romeo and Juliet.
13. Alice Munro often publishes her short stories first in The New Yorker.
14. I heard Alanis Morissette talking about her song Ironic on a radio program called CanRock yesterday.

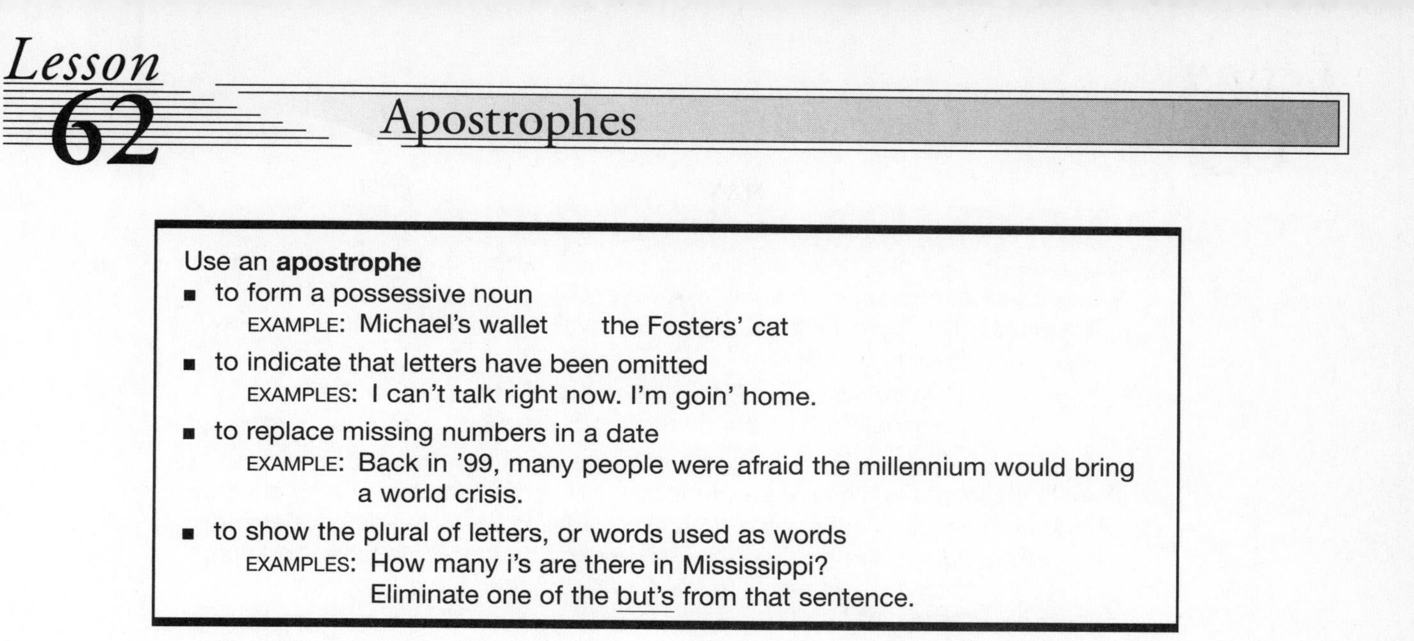

Lesson 62 Apostrophes

Use an **apostrophe**

- to form a possessive noun
  EXAMPLE: Michael's wallet   the Fosters' cat
- to indicate that letters have been omitted
  EXAMPLES: I can't talk right now. I'm goin' home.
- to replace missing numbers in a date
  EXAMPLE: Back in '99, many people were afraid the millennium would bring a world crisis.
- to show the plural of letters, or words used as words
  EXAMPLES: How many i's are there in Mississippi?
  Eliminate one of the <u>but's</u> from that sentence.

A. Add apostrophes to the sentences that follow.

1. Wont you come for a ride in Jamals 66 Chevy?
2. One of Simon and Garfunkels big hits was "Feelin Groovy."
3. Now that I have a part-time job at Yolandas Diner, Im makin good money!
4. The childrens teacher helped them learn their ABCs.
5. Remember to dot your is and cross your ts.

B. Circle any unnecessary apostrophes, and then add any apostrophes that are missing.

1. It's almost time for the dolphin to do it's trick's.
2. The menus different every week in this restaurant, because the chef's are masters of all kinds of cuisine.
3. Their stomach's were rumbling by the time the waiters brought their meals to them.
4. One more nights' work will buy me a new pair of jean's to wear to the Smith's party.
5. Sasha brought a friend whose brother got straight As.

C. Write three sentences using apostrophes. Include examples of as many different uses for apostrophes as you can in your sentences.

1. ______________________________

____

2. ______________________________

____

3. ______________________________

____

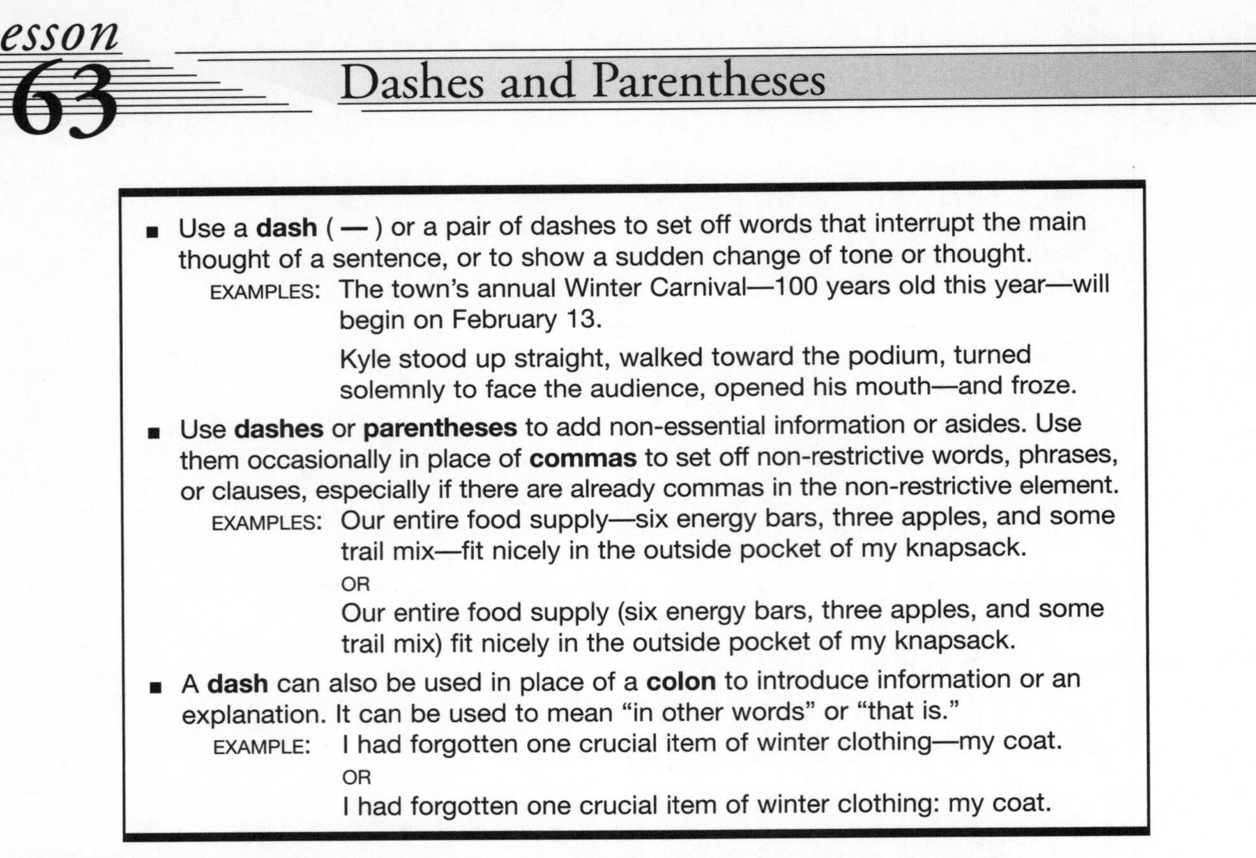

Lesson 63 Dashes and Parentheses

- Use a **dash** (—) or a pair of dashes to set off words that interrupt the main thought of a sentence, or to show a sudden change of tone or thought.

  EXAMPLES: The town's annual Winter Carnival—100 years old this year—will begin on February 13.

  Kyle stood up straight, walked toward the podium, turned solemnly to face the audience, opened his mouth—and froze.

- Use **dashes** or **parentheses** to add non-essential information or asides. Use them occasionally in place of **commas** to set off non-restrictive words, phrases, or clauses, especially if there are already commas in the non-restrictive element.

  EXAMPLES: Our entire food supply—six energy bars, three apples, and some trail mix—fit nicely in the outside pocket of my knapsack.

  OR

  Our entire food supply (six energy bars, three apples, and some trail mix) fit nicely in the outside pocket of my knapsack.

- A **dash** can also be used in place of a **colon** to introduce information or an explanation. It can be used to mean "in other words" or "that is."

  EXAMPLE: I had forgotten one crucial item of winter clothing—my coat.

  OR

  I had forgotten one crucial item of winter clothing: my coat.

A. Add dashes or parentheses where they are needed in the sentences that follow.

1. That picture frame we found out later it was an antique was bought at a garage sale for 75 cents.
2. The longhouse a long, narrow, windowless hut made from wood was the traditional dwelling of Woodland clans.
3. The car did its best choking and coughing and trying to turn over but in the end we had it towed.
4. I thought I knew every nook and cranny of this campsite but he managed to find a hiding place I had never thought of the canoe.
5. There is only one thing I detest about Mondays well, okay, two things getting up and staying up.

- Avoid overusing dashes or parentheses, or overloading sentences with non-essential information. Consider using commas, or reducing the amount of information in the sentence.

B. Rewrite the following sentences in your notebook. Find ways to eliminate the dashes and parentheses (e.g., use other punctuation or no punctuation, reword the sentence, break it into two smaller sentences, or eliminate unnecessary information).

1. Before we entered the cave—to embark on our first solo spelunking journey—we made sure we had all our supplies with us—rope, lamps, a whistle, the first-aid kit, and food.
2. My mother (who is a doctor) loves to watch medical shows on TV (her favourite show is *ER*).
3. On the other hand, Uncle Dan—he's my favourite uncle—enjoys (or at least watches) cooking shows after work, and he's a chef!
4. Of all the books we have been assigned this term, I would say *Brave New World* is the most—what shall I call it?—intriguing (although I haven't finished it yet).
5. What is most frightening—at least to me—about Huxley's vision of the future (as described in the book) is how close we have come to realizing parts of it—test-tube babies and social control, for example.

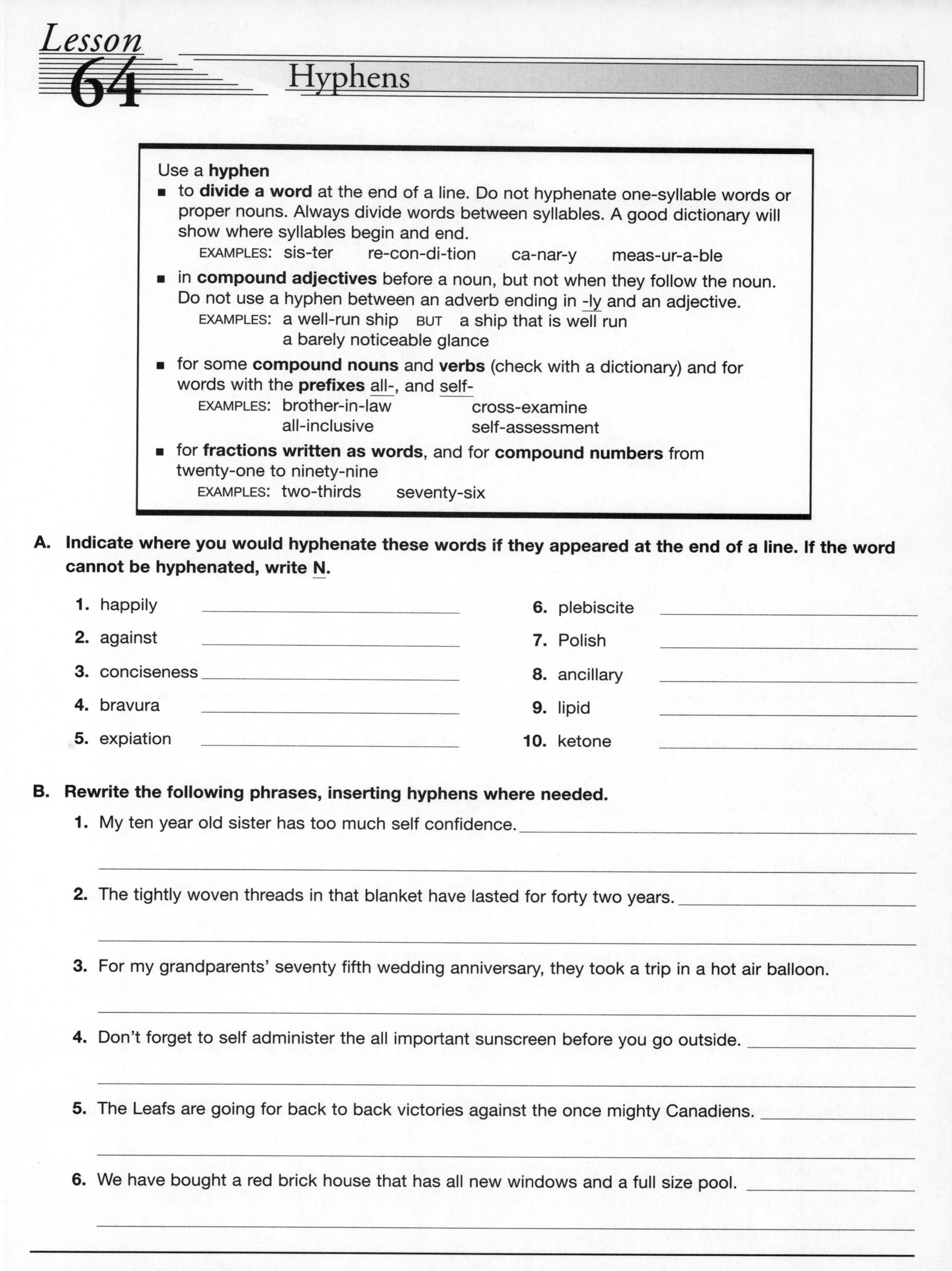

Lesson 64 Hyphens

Use a **hyphen**

- to **divide a word** at the end of a line. Do not hyphenate one-syllable words or proper nouns. Always divide words between syllables. A good dictionary will show where syllables begin and end.
  EXAMPLES: sis-ter re-con-di-tion ca-nar-y meas-ur-a-ble
- in **compound adjectives** before a noun, but not when they follow the noun. Do not use a hyphen between an adverb ending in -ly and an adjective.
  EXAMPLES: a well-run ship BUT a ship that is well run
  a barely noticeable glance
- for some **compound nouns** and **verbs** (check with a dictionary) and for words with the **prefixes** all-, and self-
  EXAMPLES: brother-in-law cross-examine
  all-inclusive self-assessment
- for **fractions written as words**, and for **compound numbers** from twenty-one to ninety-nine
  EXAMPLES: two-thirds seventy-six

A. Indicate where you would hyphenate these words if they appeared at the end of a line. If the word cannot be hyphenated, write N.

1. happily ____________
2. against ____________
3. conciseness ____________
4. bravura ____________
5. expiation ____________
6. plebiscite ____________
7. Polish ____________
8. ancillary ____________
9. lipid ____________
10. ketone ____________

B. Rewrite the following phrases, inserting hyphens where needed.

1. My ten year old sister has too much self confidence. ____________
2. The tightly woven threads in that blanket have lasted for forty two years. ____________
3. For my grandparents' seventy fifth wedding anniversary, they took a trip in a hot air balloon. ____________
4. Don't forget to self administer the all important sunscreen before you go outside. ____________
5. The Leafs are going for back to back victories against the once mighty Canadiens. ____________
6. We have bought a red brick house that has all new windows and a full size pool. ____________

Lesson 65 Semicolons and Colons

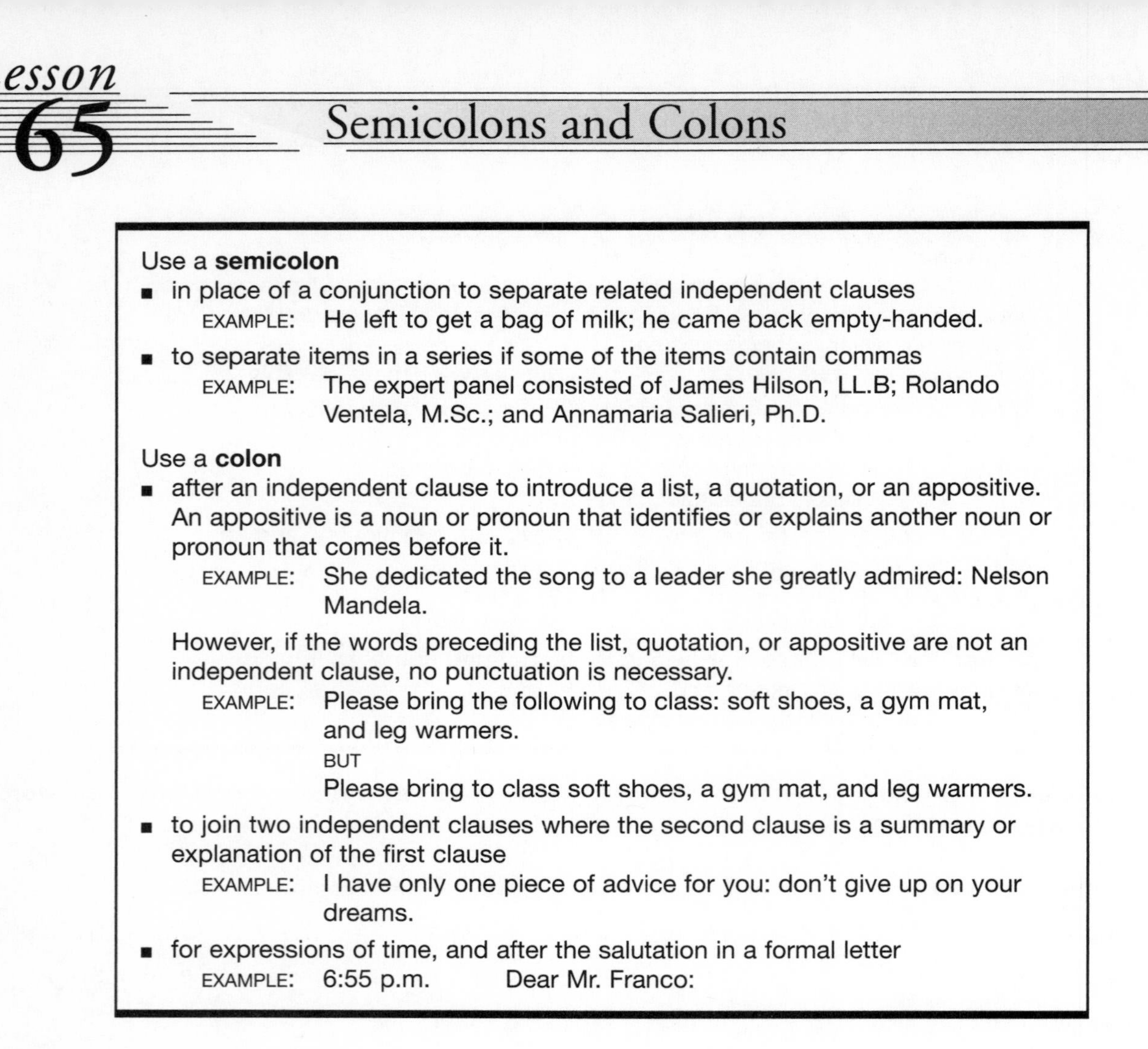

Use a **semicolon**

- in place of a conjunction to separate related independent clauses
  EXAMPLE: He left to get a bag of milk; he came back empty-handed.
- to separate items in a series if some of the items contain commas
  EXAMPLE: The expert panel consisted of James Hilson, LL.B; Rolando Ventela, M.Sc.; and Annamaria Salieri, Ph.D.

Use a **colon**

- after an independent clause to introduce a list, a quotation, or an appositive. An appositive is a noun or pronoun that identifies or explains another noun or pronoun that comes before it.
  EXAMPLE: She dedicated the song to a leader she greatly admired: Nelson Mandela.

  However, if the words preceding the list, quotation, or appositive are not an independent clause, no punctuation is necessary.
  EXAMPLE: Please bring the following to class: soft shoes, a gym mat, and leg warmers.
  BUT
  Please bring to class soft shoes, a gym mat, and leg warmers.
- to join two independent clauses where the second clause is a summary or explanation of the first clause
  EXAMPLE: I have only one piece of advice for you: don't give up on your dreams.
- for expressions of time, and after the salutation in a formal letter
  EXAMPLE: 6:55 p.m. Dear Mr. Franco:

Add semicolons and colons where they are necessary in the sentences that follow.

1. We tried the door unfortunately, it was locked.
2. We zeroed in quickly on the source of the odour my gym shoes.
3. We would like to meet at 10 30 in the board room does that time suit you?
4. Canadians call it an elevator Britons call it a lift.
5. At the end of the tournament I was left with three letters that I could not play two W's and an X.
6. Mystery writer Margaret Millar has this to say about the art of conversation: "Most conversations are simply monologues delivered in the presence of witnesses."
7. I need three of you to help out one to hold the ladder, one to read the instructions, and one to pass the tools.
8. Some examples of the kinds of vegetables we grow are white, red, and yukon gold potatoes leeks and several varieties of squash.
9. Only one person I know would eat the last cookie and leave the empty bag my brother Eugene.
10. The school is closed due to inclement weather the ski hills, however, are open.
11. We need to buy milk, eggs, and bread therefore, we may as well go to the supermarket.
12. We need to remember a few important rules don't run on the deck, don't fall in the water, and don't dive in the shallow end.

Review

A. Name three uses for capital letters and give an example of each.

1. ______________________________

____

2. ______________________________

____

3. ______________________________

____

B. Which of the following sentences does not require a question mark?

1. You are absolutely sure that you heard him correctly, are you
2. That was a lovely gesture, wasn't it
3. Ewan is arriving at what time
4. I asked him how he could possibly pass without studying
5. Does anyone really believe that a rabbit can lay eggs

C. Add commas to the following sentences. If the sentence requires no commas, write C.

1. I would have arrived here much sooner but my car broke down on the outskirts of town.
2. "That darn cat just won't come out of the tree" yelled Uncle Clem who could never bear to see an animal in danger.
3. I have always said that Canada and especially Québec produces some of the best animators in the world.
4. The park that I played in as a child which has not changed much since I was two was a children's paradise.
5. The fox had a beautiful sleek silver-tinged fur coat.
6. I'm not going to the party on Saturday because I wasn't invited.
7. I held tight to the bungee cord and took deep breaths but I couldn't stop myself from panicking.
8. "Like most right-handed hockey players" she said "I shoot left."
9. Daniel was tall and agile but had never played basketball.
10. Apparently someone has mistakenly eaten my bag of chips which I was saving for tonight.

D. Add hyphens to show where you would divide the following words if they fell at the end of a line. Use a dictionary, if necessary. If the word cannot be divided, write NO and explain why.

1. Constantinople ______________________________
2. among ______________________________
3. separate ______________________________

4. self-satisfied ______________________________

5. catatonic ______________________________

6. temerity ______________________________

7. acidic ______________________________

8. geriatric ______________________________

9. school ______________________________

10. pride ______________________________

E. Write an example of each of the following titles. Use underlining or quotation marks as necessary.

1. movie: ______________________________

2. TV situation comedy: ______________________________

3. short story: ______________________________

4. play: ______________________________

5. radio show: ______________________________

F. Add dashes and apostrophes to the following sentences, where appropriate.

1. Im not sure if we will be able to get a seat on the plane remember, its a holiday weekend but we can certainly try.
2. Your essay has too many conjunctions especially *ands* and *buts*.
3. Please dont hesitate to ask me for help with your math homework but not right now.
4. How bout makin me one of your famous peanut butter and jam sandwiches?
5. Beth and Otmar Sauer my maternal grandparents were married in 42.

G. Write two sentences to illustrate two different ways to use semicolons.

1. ______________________________

____

2. ______________________________

____

H. Write two sentences to illustrate two different ways to use colons.

1. ______________________________

____

2. ______________________________

Using What You've Learned

A. Find all the errors in punctuation and capitalization in the following paragraphs and correct them. Write the corrected paragraphs in your notebook.

On April 9 1917—easter Monday, Canadian soldiers in World War I mounted one of their most important offensives of the war. Vimy Ridge, a hill in northern France had been captured by the Germans early in the war and neither the French nor the british had been able to recapture it. The Canadians succeeded where these other armies had failed. On that fateful day, more than 3500 Canadian soldiers died and another 7000 were injured in the space of just seven hours—but the hill was their's.

Certainly, the battle was a turning point in the war, it was also, however, a turning point in Canadas' development as a country. The courageous victory of our soldier's in their first major battle gave Canadians the respect of their allies and a lasting sense of pride and self identity. Many believe, this was when Canada came of age as a nation. (among those who espouse this view is the well known historian Pierre Berton, whose book "Vimy" did much to bring the battle to the prominence it deserves in Canadian history).

Seventy five years later, the battle was commemorated by prime minister Brian Mulroney, president François Mitterand of France, and by 14 surviving veterans who still remember the day when so many of their comrades died. In his speech, Mulroney made the following plea—

> "we are here not only to keep faith with those who made the supreme sacrifice, but to rededicate ourselves to the values and ideals that they so courageously defended. Their contribution to the Allied victory in the First World War will be celebrated wherever men and women discuss freedom and the bravery of those who fought to preserve it."

(Source: Adapted from CBC *News in Review Resource Guide*, May 1992, page 72.)

B. Rewrite each of the following quotations by former prime minister Brian Mulroney, adding single or double quotation marks, square brackets, and ellipsis points where necessary.

1. **Original:** Vimy was the first battle in which Canadians fought as an independent force, and it was a victory of such heroic proportions that it signalled to the world the coming of age of Canada as a promising and prosperous nation.

   Quotation: According to Mulroney, Vimy was the first battle in which Canadians fought as an independent force, and it signalled to the world the coming of age of Canada.

2. **Original:** As a former prime minister of Canada, the Right Honourable Arthur Meighen said so eloquently, not long after Vimy: "No words can add to their fame, nor so long as gratitude holds a place in men's hearts, can our forgetfulness be suffered to detract from their renown."

   Quotation: Mulroney made reference to another former prime minister in his speech. As a former prime minister of Canada, the Right Honourable Arthur Meighen said not long after Vimy, No words can add to their fame, nor so long as gratitude holds a place in men's hearts, can our forgetfulness be suffered to detract from their renown.

3. **Original:** No monument, no ceremony, could ever do justice to the historic contribution that the heroes of Vimy, and all our soldiers who died in war, made to our country and to the cause of freedom.

   Quotation: He reminded the crowd that no monument, no ceremony, could ever do justice to the historic contribution that the heroes of Vimy made to Canada.

C. Choose a quotation from the Vimy text in part A. Write a sentence to introduce the quotation, and then write the excerpt, using correct punctuation and capitalization. Illustrate the correct use of square brackets and ellipses in your excerpt.

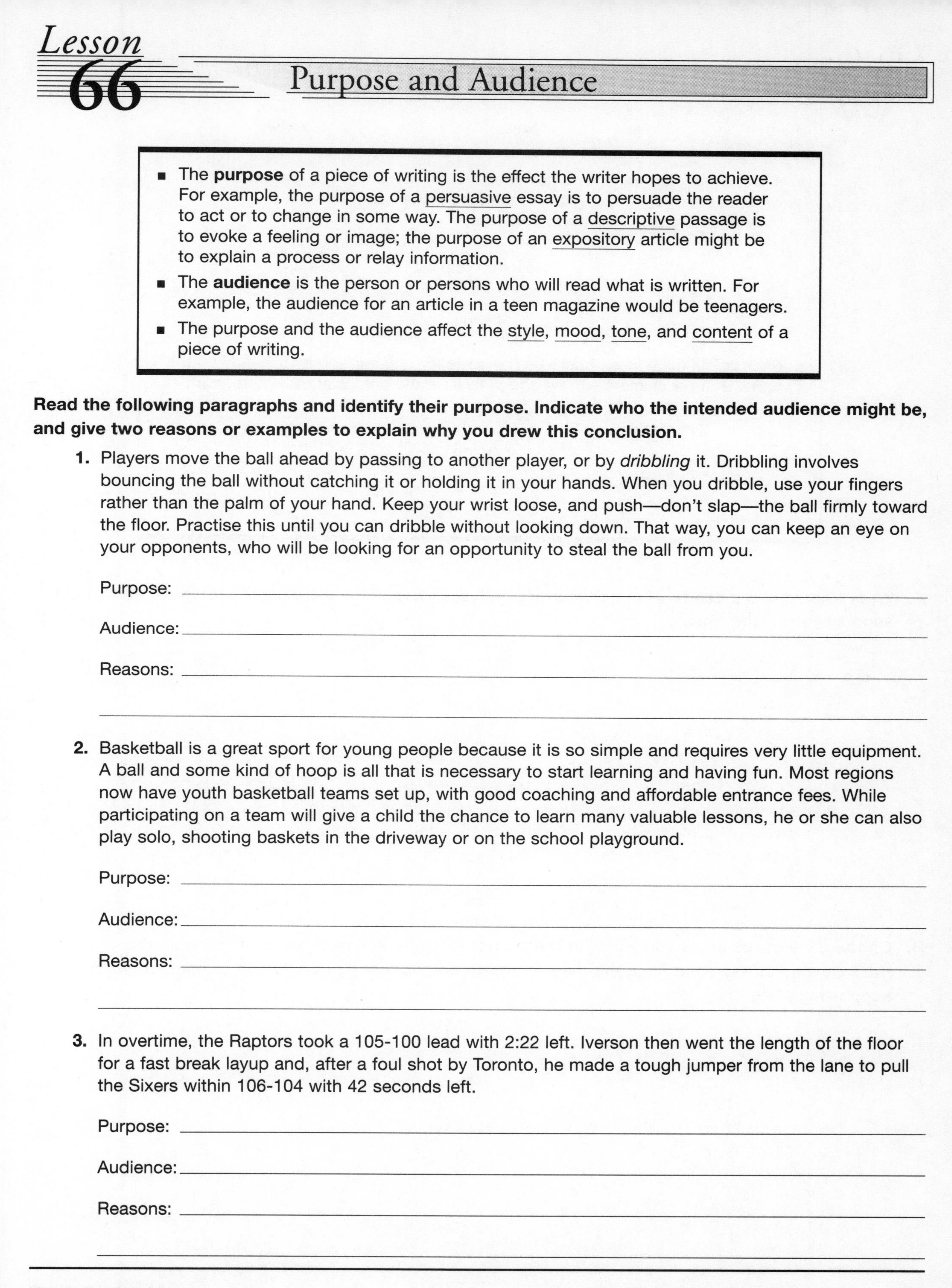

Lesson 66 Purpose and Audience

- The **purpose** of a piece of writing is the effect the writer hopes to achieve. For example, the purpose of a persuasive essay is to persuade the reader to act or to change in some way. The purpose of a descriptive passage is to evoke a feeling or image; the purpose of an expository article might be to explain a process or relay information.
- The **audience** is the person or persons who will read what is written. For example, the audience for an article in a teen magazine would be teenagers.
- The purpose and the audience affect the style, mood, tone, and content of a piece of writing.

Read the following paragraphs and identify their purpose. Indicate who the intended audience might be, and give two reasons or examples to explain why you drew this conclusion.

1. Players move the ball ahead by passing to another player, or by *dribbling* it. Dribbling involves bouncing the ball without catching it or holding it in your hands. When you dribble, use your fingers rather than the palm of your hand. Keep your wrist loose, and push—don't slap—the ball firmly toward the floor. Practise this until you can dribble without looking down. That way, you can keep an eye on your opponents, who will be looking for an opportunity to steal the ball from you.

   Purpose: ____________________

   Audience: ____________________

   Reasons: ____________________

   ____

2. Basketball is a great sport for young people because it is so simple and requires very little equipment. A ball and some kind of hoop is all that is necessary to start learning and having fun. Most regions now have youth basketball teams set up, with good coaching and affordable entrance fees. While participating on a team will give a child the chance to learn many valuable lessons, he or she can also play solo, shooting baskets in the driveway or on the school playground.

   Purpose: ____________________

   Audience: ____________________

   Reasons: ____________________

   ____

3. In overtime, the Raptors took a 105-100 lead with 2:22 left. Iverson then went the length of the floor for a fast break layup and, after a foul shot by Toronto, he made a tough jumper from the lane to pull the Sixers within 106-104 with 42 seconds left.

   Purpose: ____________________

   Audience: ____________________

   Reasons: ____________________

   ____

Lesson 67 Clustering

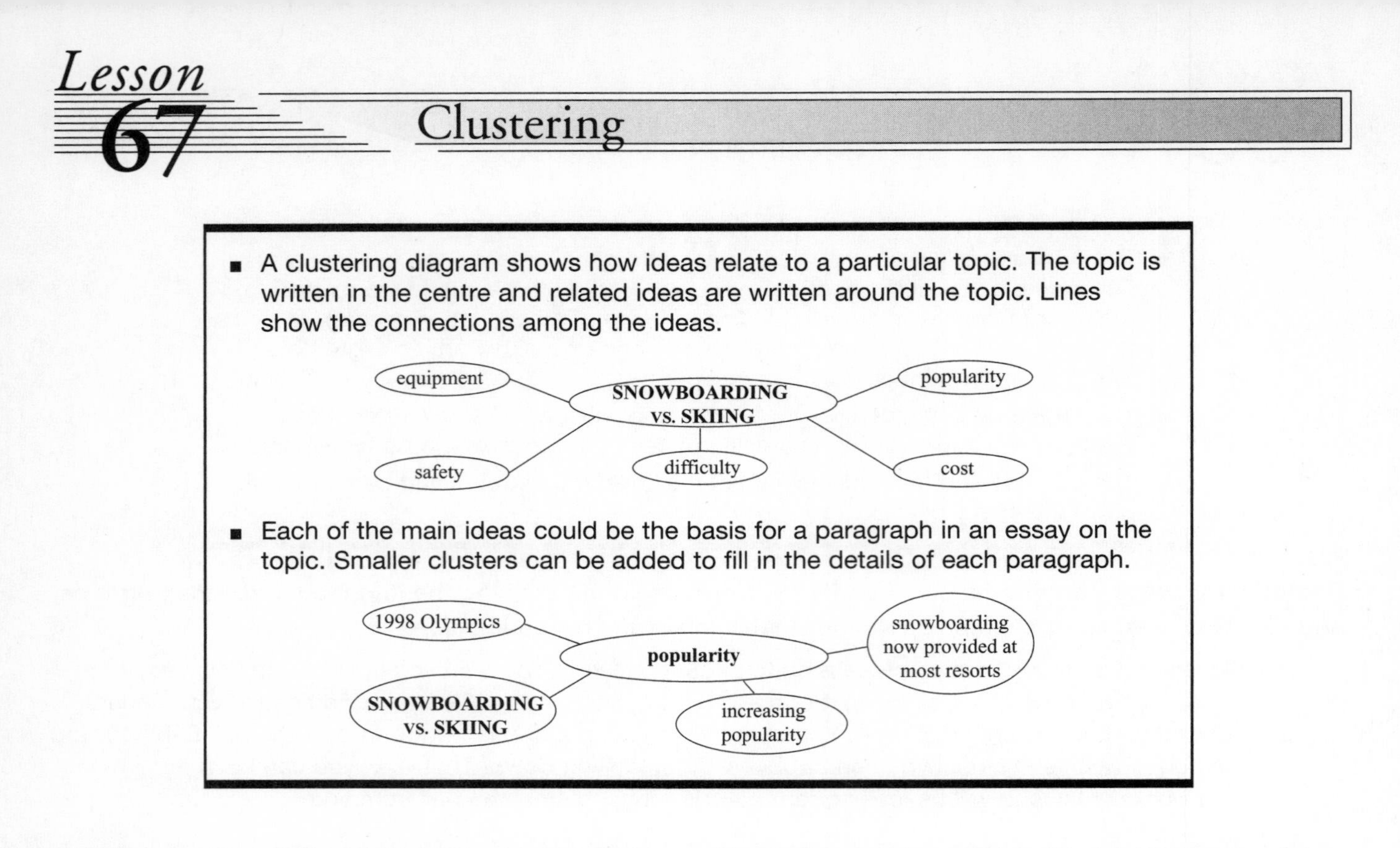

- A clustering diagram shows how ideas relate to a particular topic. The topic is written in the centre and related ideas are written around the topic. Lines show the connections among the ideas.
- Each of the main ideas could be the basis for a paragraph in an essay on the topic. Smaller clusters can be added to fill in the details of each paragraph.

A. Write a topic in the centre of the cluster that follows. Then, fill in the cluster with ideas that would support your main topic.

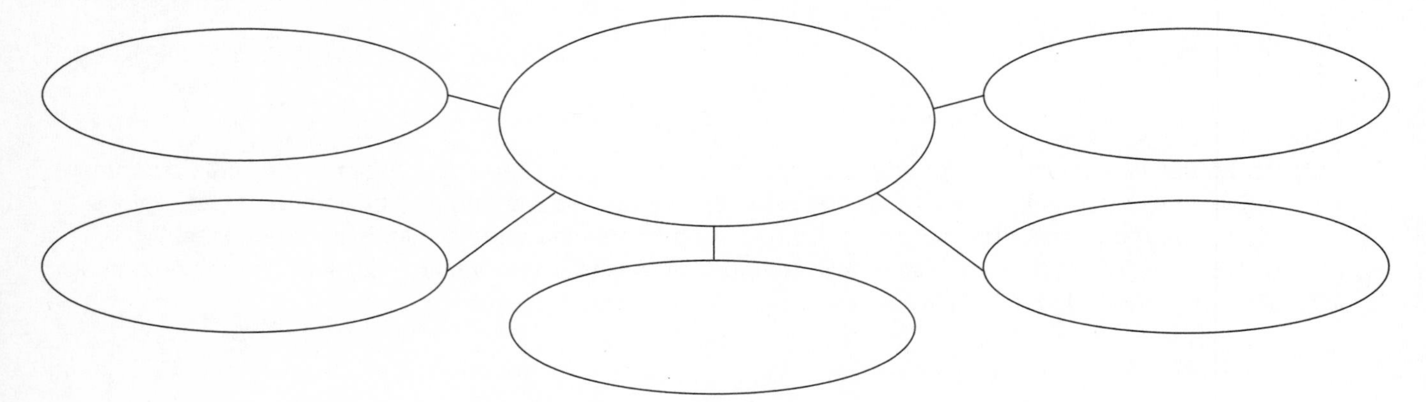

B. Choose one of the ideas you wrote in the cluster diagram in part A, place it in the centre of the following cluster, and fill in the diagrams with details that you could use to back up your supporting idea.

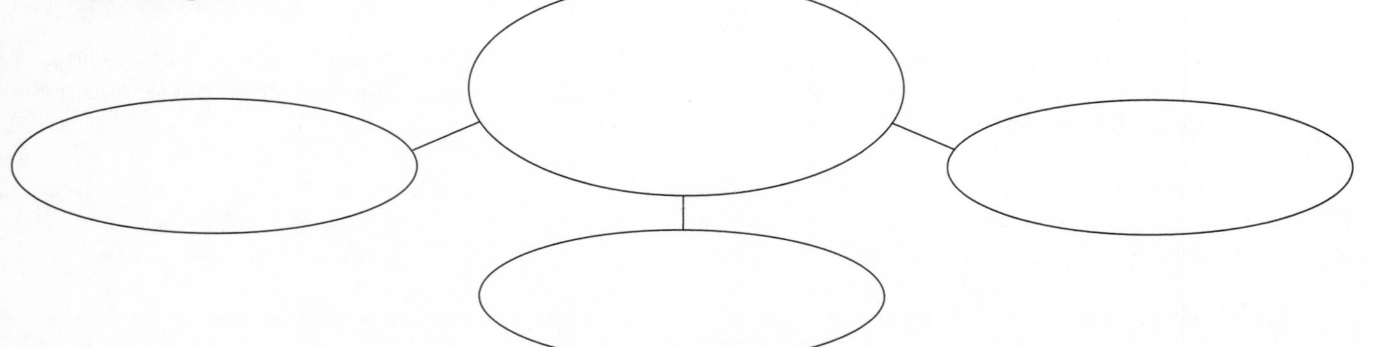

Lesson 68 Patterns of Development

Essays and other kinds of writing can be organized in various ways, depending on the subject matter, the purpose, and the intended audience. The following patterns can be used to organize a single paragraph or a whole essay:

- chronological or time sequence, (e.g., narratives and factual accounts)
- spatial or location order (e.g., descriptions)
- by feature or characteristic (e.g., comparisons, descriptions)
- by relevance or importance (e.g., persuasive writing, news stories, business writing)
- cause–effect (e.g., science reports, explanations, instructions)

A. Identify the pattern of development in each of the following paragraphs.

1. Most shampoos scored well when it came to creating lather. We found greater differences, however, in the ability of different brands to leave the hair easy to comb. Only a few brands we felt really lived up to our expectations in this regard. As for smell, this is a largely subjective area, but our testers tended to prefer two or three brands over others for the clean smell that was left in their hair.

   Pattern: ______________________________

2. Our current transit problems are a direct result of the city plan for housing development. By encouraging builders to continue building large single-family dwellings in sprawling suburbs, Council has made it difficult if not impossible for the Transit Authority to provide viable bus services in these areas. The lower population base means ridership is minimal; on some runs, there are no more than two or three people being picked up on an entire route.

   Pattern: ______________________________

B. Write a description of one of the following using a spatial pattern of development.

- a celebrity's facial features
- a wooded area
- a busy street corner
- your living room

____

____

____

____

____

____

____

____

____

____

Lesson 69 Outlining

- Before you write, organize your thoughts by making an **outline**. An outline consists of the title of the topic, headings for the main ideas, and subheadings for the supporting details.
- Main headings are listed after Roman numerals. Subheadings are listed after capital letters. Details are listed after Arabic numerals.

EXAMPLE:

Topic: Should the voting age be lowered to 16?

Main heading: I. Arguments in favour of lowering the voting age

Subheading: A. Rights should match responsibilities

Details:
1. Sixteen-year-olds accountable to society for their actions
2. Can leave school and join the workforce at 16

Subheading: B. Kids have concerns but no voice

Details:
1. environmental issues
2. equal rights for youth

Main heading: II. Arguments against lowering the voting age

Subheading: A. Too young to make mature judgments about politicians

Details:
1. most have not finished education
2. little life experience

Subheading: B. Might not take the responsibility seriously

Choose a topic that interests you. Then write an outline for that topic in the space below, using the example outline as a guide.

Lesson 70 Formulating a Thesis

- A **thesis** is a statement of the main idea of an essay or paper. The thesis is usually stated in the opening paragraph, and the topic sentence of each paragraph that follows enlarges upon or supports the idea it expresses.
- Often, the thesis suggests a method of development for the paragraphs that follow.

  EXAMPLE: Hans Selye identified a three-stage human response to stress, which he called the General Adaptation Syndrome.
  (This thesis sentence identifies the topic, and suggests that the paragraphs that will follow it will look at each of the three stages.)

A. Write a thesis statement for each of the topics below.

1. A comparison of two sports

____

____

2. A Canadian hero

____

____

3. A character in a novel you have been reading in class

____

____

B. Think of your own topics, and then write thesis statements that relate to them.

1. Topic: ______________________________

   Thesis: ______________________________

   ____

   ____

2. Topic: ______________________________

   Thesis: ______________________________

   ____

   ____

3. Topic: ______________________________

   Thesis: ______________________________

   ____

   ____

- A **thesis** should be broad enough to include all the subtopics, information, or arguments in the essay. However, it should be narrow enough to allow you to deal with it thoroughly in the space available.
- Avoid using extreme terms such as all, never, and always in a thesis, unless you are sure you can back up what you are saying.

  EXAMPLE: **Too broad:** All stress research today owes its existence to the work of Hans Selye.
  (It would be almost impossible to prove such a general statement.)
  Too narrow: Hans Selye was the first to coin the term "stress" in relation to human beings.
  (This is an interesting fact, but it does not leave much room for the writer to expand upon it.)

C. For each topic, underline the sentence that would make the best thesis for a short essay.

1. Topic: Looking for a job
   a) A successful job search requires both preparation and perseverance.
   b) Looking for a job is hard work.
   c) The unemployment rate for students is usually higher than the national average.
2. Topic: Canada's system of government
   a) Canada was founded in 1867.
   b) Canada has the best system of government in the world.
   c) Canada is both a constitutional monarchy and a parliamentary democracy.

D. Write a thesis that expresses the main idea behind each of the following groups of sentences.

1. Topic sentence 1: Many video games require strong problem-solving skills.

   Topic sentence 2: Manipulating a controller or mouse can increase the user's manual dexterity.

   Topic sentence 3: Often, games can be played with a partner, and the numerous clubs for video-game enthusiasts give players more opportunities for social interaction.

   Thesis: ____

   ____

   ____

   ____

   ____

2. Topic sentence 1: The family is the first agent of socialization that most of us encounter.

   Topic sentence 2: Schools have a strong socializing influence as well.

   Topic sentence 3: As we get older, our peers become increasingly important as agents of socialization.

   Thesis: ____

   ____

   ____

   ____

   ____

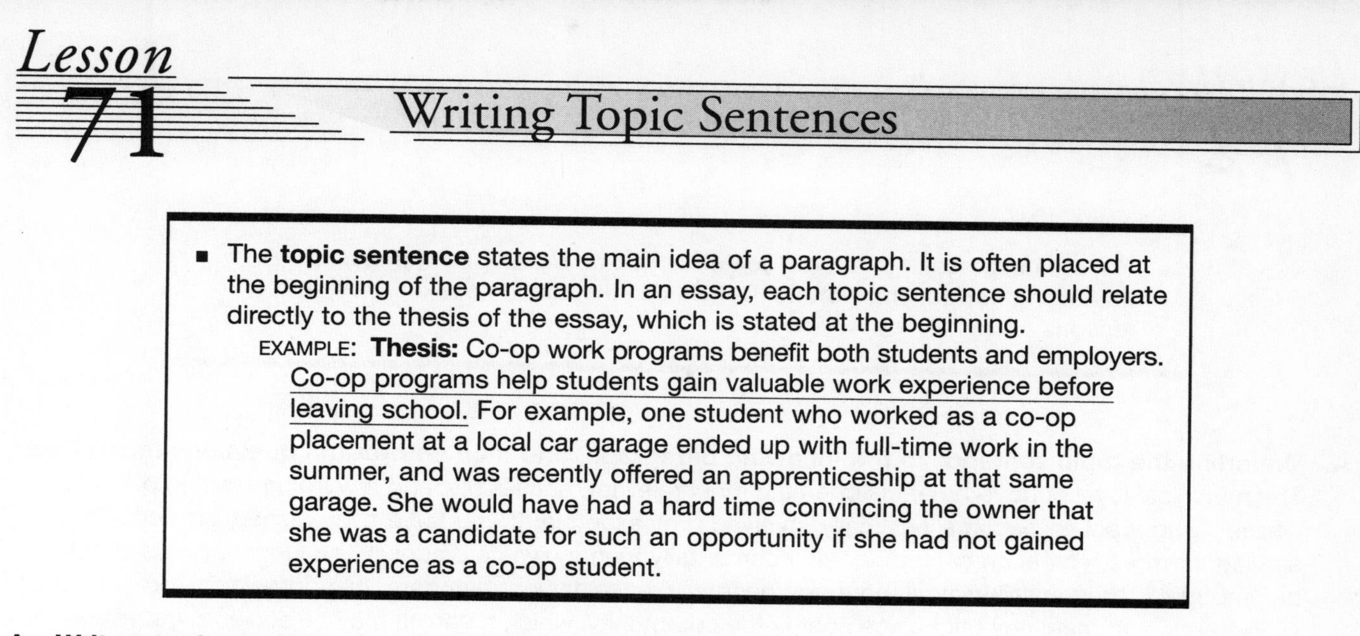

Lesson 71 Writing Topic Sentences

- The **topic sentence** states the main idea of a paragraph. It is often placed at the beginning of the paragraph. In an essay, each topic sentence should relate directly to the thesis of the essay, which is stated at the beginning.

  EXAMPLE: **Thesis:** Co-op work programs benefit both students and employers.
  Co-op programs help students gain valuable work experience before leaving school. For example, one student who worked as a co-op placement at a local car garage ended up with full-time work in the summer, and was recently offered an apprenticeship at that same garage. She would have had a hard time convincing the owner that she was a candidate for such an opportunity if she had not gained experience as a co-op student.

A. Write a topic sentence for each group of related sentences.

1. Some psychologists work in universities, conducting primary research on human and animal subjects. Others are hired by industry or businesses. These applied psychologists suggest ways to make the work environment more appealing, and to increase productivity among employees. Still others employ their skills in marketing products for consumption. Finally, some psychologists work in private practice, counselling individuals and helping them to use psychological principles to overcome difficulties in their lives.

   Topic sentence: ______________________________

   ____

2. Wetlands contain a wealth of nutrients, which make them a perfect place for fish, shrimp, crabs, and waterfowl to nest. They also help humans by absorbing excess water from storms and floods, and by acting as a natural filter for pollutants. Far from useless swampland, they are areas that need our protection, especially since more and more wetlands are disappearing under the pressure for housing and development.

   Topic sentence: ______________________________

   ____

3. Joy Kogawa, like her fictional character Naomi Nakane, is a Canadian of Japanese descent. Like Naomi, Kogawa and her family were forced into internment camps in the B.C. interior after the bombing of Pearl Harbour during World War II. Kogawa notes another similarity between herself and the little girl in *Obasan*: "'Like Naomi, I became a person who would not speak, would not ask a question, did not expect to be heard.'"

   Topic sentence: ______________________________

   ____

B. Choose one of the thesis statements you wrote in Lesson 70, and then write three topic sentences in your notebook that relate to it.

Lesson 72 Writing Supporting Details

- The idea expressed in a topic sentence can be developed with sentences containing **supporting details**. Details can include facts, examples, and reasons.

A. Underline the topic sentence in the following paragraph, and then answer the questions that follow.

The municipal level of government is often the most relevant, accessible, and rewarding starting place for citizens who want to become politically involved. For example, if you have ever wished for better bus service, or more recreation centres, or environmentally friendly waste disposal, then local politics should be important to you. Municipal councils generally have fewer members than provincial or federal legislatures, and meetings take place right in the community, which means it may be easier to get access to the key decision-makers. Finally, municipal politics is rewarding because it allows ordinary citizens to influence the decisions that affect their lives and communities every day.

1. Identify one supporting detail that is a fact.

____

____

2. Identify one supporting detail that is a reason.

____

____

3. Identify one supporting detail that uses examples.

____

____

B. Read the topic sentences that follow, and then write three supporting details for each one. Use full sentences.

1. Old-fashioned print books still have some advantages over digital information sources.

____

____

____

2. We can all begin planning for our future careers before we finish high school.

____

____

____

____

Lesson 73

Using Transition Words

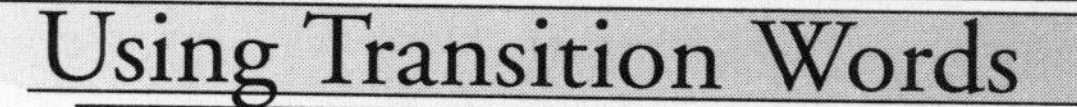

- **Transitions** are words or phrases that connect ideas. Transitions help the reader clearly understand relationships such as time, space, emphasis, example, contrast, comparison, effect, and addition.

A. Fill in the blanks in the chart below with other examples of transitional words and phrases.

Category	Examples
1. Time	before, after, ______, ______
2. Location	here, there, ______, ______
3. Example	for instance, ______, ______
4. Sequence	first, ______, ______
5. Contrast	however, ______, ______
6. Comparison	likewise, ______, ______
7. Effect	consequently, thus, ______, ______
8. Addition	furthermore, ______, ______
9. Conclusion	in conclusion, ______, ______

B. Underline the transition words and phrases in the following paragraph.

What does it mean to be a good citizen? First and foremost, citizenship means exercising your right to vote. However, being a citizen in a democracy means a lot more than that. You also need to remain informed about issues that affect your life and the lives of those around you. For example, let's say a wooded area in your neighbourhood that you like to hike in is slated for development. Is it enough to simply leave its fate to the politicians you elected? On the contrary, it is your duty to let your elected representative know your feelings on the issue. Otherwise, how can you expect him or her to do the job of representing your wishes? In the end, we all get the government that we deserve.

C. Write a paragraph outlining your response to the ideas in part B. Use transitional words or phrases to connect your ideas. Underline the transitions.

____

____

____

____

____

____

____

Lesson 74

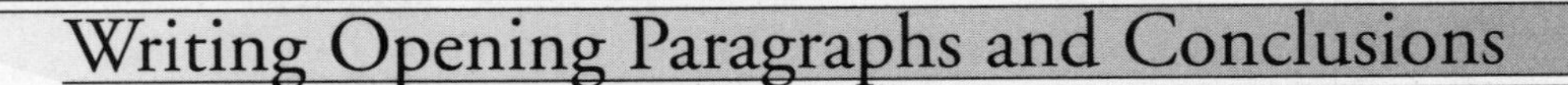

Writing Opening Paragraphs and Conclusions

- In addition to presenting the thesis, the **opening paragraph** of an essay or report should grab the interest of the reader and set the tone for the writing that follows.
- Some techniques for creating interest include telling an anecdote, describing a scene, presenting a surprising or interesting fact or statistic that relates to the topic, posing a question or series of questions, or drawing a connection between the topic of the paper and the lives of the intended audience.
- Many writers find it easier to write the introduction after they have written the rest of the paper or article.

  EXAMPLE: In Western culture, wolves have long been associated with the deceitful, conniving, and dangerous creatures of fairy tales, or with the frightening mythical creature known as the werewolf. Perhaps this is why we have often treated them so atrociously. Western settlers, for example, used traps, poison, and other methods to hunt the wolf to near extinction. But wolves don't really deserve their bad reputation, according to experts. On the contrary, they are intelligent, social creatures who rarely attack humans. In fact, we are more of a threat to them than they have ever been to us. We need to re-evaluate our image of the wolf, and focus on preserving, rather than fearing, these amazing animals.

  (Source: "Canadian Wolves Go South: Reclaiming Habitat." *News in Review*. March 1996, pages 42–51.)

A. Write an introductory paragraph for a short paper on one of the topics below, or a topic of your choice (you may use the topic for which you created an outline in Lesson 69). Your intended audience is students your age. Include an attention-grabber as well as a thesis in your introduction.

- bullying in schools
- lowering the voting age
- snowboarding vs. skiing
- responsibilities of citizenship
- ecological importance of wetlands
- advantages of high school co-op programs

____

____

____

____

____

____

____

____

B. Write a different introductory paragraph in your notebook for the same topic. This time, your audience is the general public.

- The **conclusion** of an essay, article, or report usually summarizes or reinforces the main argument that has been presented. It may refer back to an image or idea that was used in the introduction.
- The conclusion should not introduce new information or ideas that have not already been discussed in the body.

  EXAMPLE: We cannot do anything to change the way we have treated wolves in the past. We can, however, and we must, do everything we can to preserve those that remain. To many aboriginal people, the wolf is a symbol of freedom and survival, good providers who look after their family. We would do well to adopt their approach, moving beyond the "big bad wolf" of our childhood to a more positive image of these magnificent creatures.

C. Read the persuasive article on banning pesticides in Lesson 75. Then write a conclusion for the article.

Lesson 75

Persuasive Writing

- **Persuasive writing** tries to convince the reader to accept an opinion or point of view.
- Persuasive writing uses a mixture of emotional appeals and reason to convince the reader. An emotional appeal may take the form of words, images, or ideas that carry strong positive or negative connotations. Another common persuasive technique is to appeal to authority to back a statement.
- The strongest arguments in favour of your thesis should be arranged for maximum effectiveness. Beginning with weaker arguments and building up to a strong conclusion works well if the audience is sympathetic. If the audience starts out hostile to the idea being presented and needs to be convinced of its validity, many writers prefer to position their stronger arguments at the beginning and end of their essay.

Read the persuasive essay that follows, and then complete the activities on the next page.

Pesticides should be banned because they represent a considerable health risk, and they are inadequately regulated. Moreover, more environmentally friendly methods of pest control are already in existence or being tested.

Innumerable scientific studies have shown that some pesticides have adverse effects on health. According to the Nova Scotia Allergy and Environmental Health Association, these effects range from mild headaches to damage to the nervous system. Pesticide companies claim that when used properly, their products are safe and effective. However, it is impossible to regulate the safe use of a product that is widely available to consumers. Do we want to take that kind of risk?

While pesticide companies point out that Health Canada requires them to perform more than 200 different tests on pesticides before they reach the market, there is reason to believe that the regulation of pesticides is less than perfect. The approval of pesticides prior to the 1960s was much more lax than it is today. Yet many of the chemicals that were approved then are still in use today, and have never been subject to review. According to the Nova Scotia Allergy and Environmental Health Association, the tests performed today do not adequately test for effects on humans, especially on the central nervous system and the immune system. And the World Health Organization estimates that pesticides cause at least 20 000 deaths each year worldwide.

A ban on the cosmetic use of pesticides would not cause great hardship to consumers. Granted, the pesticide industry would suffer; however, a number of these companies are already selling natural methods of lawn care. Alternatives to pesticides include ingredients such as rhubarb, soap, and garlic; and innovative methods of plant control, such as directing a stream of hot steam on them to prevent their growth. And scientists are working on developing a fungus that kills dandelions without harming other plants or humans.

(Source: Adapted from <cbc.ca/consumers/indepth/lawn> and Nova Scotia Allergy and Environmental Health Association (NSAEHA) presentation to Halifax Regional Municipality, March 28, 2000.)

1. Identify and record the thesis sentence.

2. Identify the three main arguments.

3. Find an example of an emotional appeal or loaded words.

4. Identify two places where the writer anticipates the arguments of those who are against banning pesticides.

5. Find an example where the author has appealed to authority to strengthen an argument.

6. Which of the arguments presented do you think is the most persuasive?

7. Which of the arguments is least persuasive?

8. Based on this analysis, do you think the essay is intended for a hostile or a receptive audience? Explain.

Lesson 76 Formal and Informal Writing

Formal writing

- is used for essays, reports, business letters, and official documents
- is often (though not always) written in the third person (he, she, it, one) rather than first person (I) or second person (you)
- uses standard Canadian English, and avoids colloquialisms and slang expressions
- often has a smooth, regular rhythm with a variety of sentence structures and lengths
- carefully follows the conventions of grammar and punctuation, and avoids sentence fragments, contractions, and abbreviations

A. Rewrite the following paragraphs in a more formal style to make them suitable for an essay or formal report.

It's probably not news to you, but they tell me that laughing can do wonders for your health. It seems some shrinks have finally figured out that a good belly laugh can help you chill out. In the workplace, a little humour can help to build team spirit and boost morale. And that's good for the bottom line. So, what else is new? We knew that, right? Well, what you might not have realized is that laughter can even help you fight off real serious illnesses. Even cancer, or heart disease. It's like this: laughing gives the immune system a boost, and encourages it to produce cells that fight disease. It also lowers blood pressure.

It's weird, though: it's like we lose our ability to laugh as time goes on. Kids laugh on average like about 400 times a day, while with grown-ups it's only like about 15 times a day. What's going on? If we could all just get a grip and stop taking life so seriously, we'd live healthier lives. And happier ones.

(Source: Adapted from "Take It Seriously: A Healthy Dose of Humour Can Heal" by Kevin Davis, <www.usaweekend.com/97_issues/970601/970601health_humour.html>)

Informal writing

- is used for personal letters, dialogue, and sometimes for articles in magazines
- is often (though not always) written in the first person (I) rather than the third person (he, she, it, one), and is more likely than formal writing to address the reader directly as you
- often uses colloquial expressions, and may even include some slang expressions if these will be understood by the intended reader
- has a rhythm that imitates the rhythm of casual speech, often using sentence fragments
- sometimes breaks conventions of grammar and punctuation to more closely imitate conversational English, and frequently uses contractions and abbreviations
- Most writing has some informal and some formal traits. The degree of formality depends on the purpose for writing and the intended audience.

B. Rewrite the following formal account as an informal article for a school newspaper or teen Web site.

On April 2, 1988, Remy Bricka of France undertook to set the record for walking on water. In order to perform this amazing feat, Bricka wore a pair of polyester floats on his feet, and had a sail about the size of a kite. He also had a small "survival pod" in case of emergency. He began his trek on the island of Tenerife, off the coast of Spain. Fifty-nine days later, he walked onto the shore of Trinidad, having covered a total of 5636 kilometres. When he arrived, Bricka was in a state of delirium. Apparently, he had brought no food or water with him on his trip. He had relied on a pump to filter seawater, and ate plankton or the occasional fish that landed on his pod.

Despite the appalling conditions he endured on his first trek, Bricka later attempted to cross the Pacific Ocean from Los Angeles, in the United States, to Sydney, Australia. However, after about 4000 kilometres, weather conditions forced him to abandon the trip.

Lesson 77 Revising and Proofreading

- **Revising** gives you a chance to rethink and review what you have written and to improve your writing. Revise by adding words and information, by taking out unnecessary words and information, and by moving words, sentences, and paragraphs around.
- **Proofreading** has to do with checking spelling, punctuation, grammar, and capitalization. Use proofreader's marks to show changes needed in your writing.

Proofreader's Marks

≡	capitalize		take something out		transpose (switch)
/	lower case	SP	correct spelling		add an apostrophe
	add a comma	¶	indent new paragraph		close space
⊙	add a period	→	move	#	add space
^	insert something				

A. Rewrite the following paragraphs in your notebook, correcting the errors by following the proofreader's marks.

For most of us, most of the time, the flu is just a niusance. It make's us feel lousey, and keeps us off school or work for about a weak. but for some people—the very young the old and those with compormised imune systems it can be a killer. That's because the Virus can cause other problems, such as asma, which can be deadly, or pneumonia.

Every so often, a flu bug comes a long to which we have poor resistence, the result may be a pandemic—infection that is so widespread, it effects millions of people in 1918, the spanish influenza killed 30 million people, in 1967, another 1.5 million People died from a different strain of flue. Is it possible that another pan demic is on the way

¶ Nobody knows but health officials dont want to take any chances. That is why why flu shots are being promoted lately in many regions of canada. The hope isthat by vacsinating a large number of people, we can avoid the high mortality rate that a major out break might bring—if it comes and when.

B. Read the paragraphs below. Use proofreader's marks to revise and proofread the paragraphs. Then write the corrected paragraphs in your notebook.

People have always had an intrest in, and a need for, codes. ancient greek and arab civilizations developped methods of encryption—writing codes—that tookseveral centuries to immerge else where. those involved in cryptography over over the years have included language experts phisicists theologians chess masters and crossword puzzle fanaticks. Julius caesar invented a method of encodeing messages, and so did the american statesman thomas Jefferson. The Classic horror story writer Edgar Allan Poe have an interest in codes, and Alan Turing the father of the modern computer worked on code-making and breaking during World War II

The second world war was a very exiting time for code-breaker's. Adolf Hitlers army used electromagnetic methods of encoding message's. This allowed themto keep their messages completely inaccessible to their enemys for a while, despite the hugeeffort by the Allies to brake their code. German Scientists developped a machine, known as Enigma, to encode there messages the story of how the german code was finaly brokenis as full of Drama as the most exciting battle's on land or sea.

Since then, mathematics has been used create even more secure methods of Encryption. This has become important in the age of Inter net comercial activity. Many people feel insecure abut sending credit card and other personal information still over the Internet, even if a sight is privacy protected. And perhaps they have reason. While huge imporvements have ben made in our ability to encrypt information, there will always be some one who managers to break the code. It will be up to others work even even harder to create new methods for keeping are secrets.

Review

A. Complete the cluster diagram below, using one of the following topics:

- school in the future
- what you can do to help the environment
- why everyone should get a personal holiday on their birthday
- an invention you would like to see
- a comparison of two schools, neighbourhoods, or cities

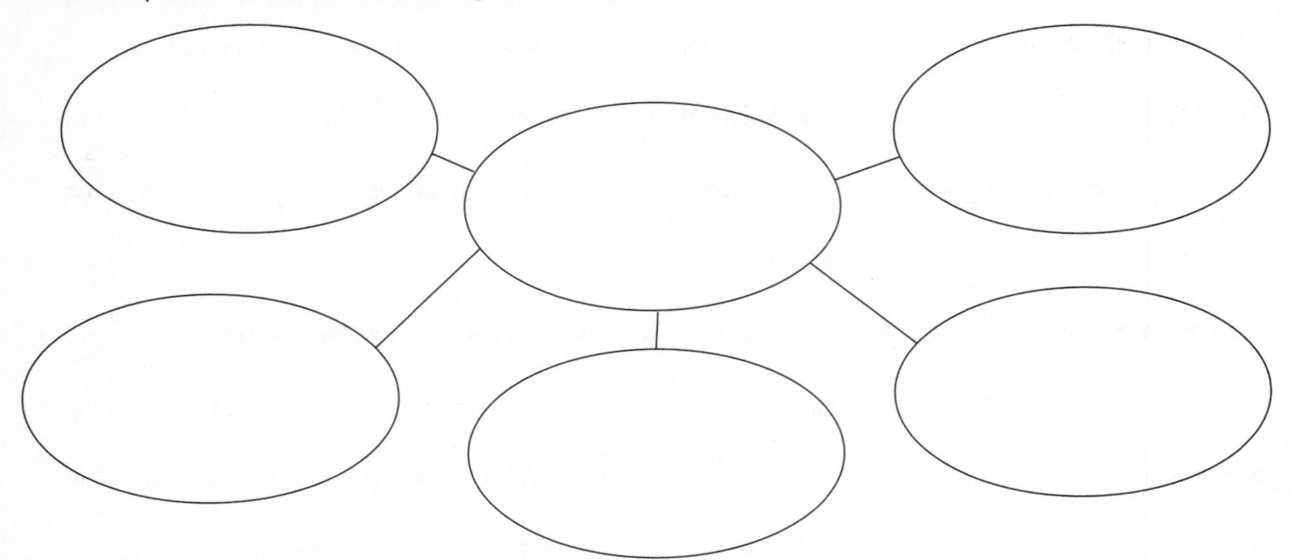

B. Write an outline based on your cluster diagram.

Topic:

I.

A.

B.

II.

A.

B.

C. Write a thesis statement based on your outline.

D. Match each writing topic with an appropriate pattern of development

1.	chronological	(a)	a description of a house that is for sale
2.	spatial	(b)	an essay that seeks to persuade the reader that the local library deserves more funding
3.	cause–effect	(c)	a comparison of two automobiles for a consumer magazine
4.	by feature	(d)	a report relating the events surrounding a car accident
5.	by importance	(e)	a science report explaining photosynthesis

1. ________ 2. ________ 3. ________ 4. ________ 5. ________

E. Read the persuasive paragraph below. Then complete the activities that follow.

Employers should consider hiring young people as part-time and summer employees for several reasons. First, young people are often quick learners with no preconceived ideas of what the job entails. Second, young people tend to be energetic and willing to work hard. Third, employers can pay such employees a lower minimum wage than they would pay adult workers. Finally, hiring youth is an investment in the future. By giving a young person a chance, companies can ensure that they will have a loyal and well-trained work force in the future.

1. Who is the intended audience for this paragraph, and what is the intended purpose?

____

____

____

2. Does this paragraph use reasons, examples, or facts to persuade the audience?

____

____

____

3. Identify the four transition words used in the paragraph.

____

____

____

4. Identify the topic sentence.

____

____

____

F. **Rewrite the paragraph in part E using a more informal tone. Your intended reader is students who are preparing for job interviews for summer employment.**

G. **Read the paragraph below. Use proofreader's marks to revise and proofread the paragraph. Then write the corrected paragraph.**

Have youever wonderd why your bod y gets hot when youre ill. It begins with the white blood cels. When they sense that an invador is present, They send out a signal tothe Brain by releaseing a substance called interleuken this singal is received by the hypothalamus, which is the temperture control centre of the brain. The Hypothalamus responds byproducing prostaglandin which raises the temperature of the body. We shivver because the prostaglandin increases our mussle tone.

Using What You've Learned

A. Create an outline for an essay with the following thesis. Your outline should have three main ideas, with supporting details for each.

Thesis: The keys to creating a world free of racism are education, exposure to other cultures, and setting a good example.

B. Write a topic sentence for each of the main ideas in your outline. Then add your supporting details in sentence form. Underline the transitional words or phrases you use.

1. Topic sentence: ____________________

   Body: ____________________

2. Topic sentence: ____________________

   Body: ____________________

3. Topic sentence: ______________________________

____

Body: ______________________________

____

____

____

____

C. Write an introduction for your essay that grabs the reader's interest and includes the thesis.

Introduction: ______________________________

____

____

____

____

D. Write a conclusion that summarizes or reinforces your main points.

Conclusion: ______________________________

____

____

____

____

E. Revise and proofread the introduction, conclusion, and the three paragraphs you wrote. Then recopy the final draft in the space below. Attach extra sheets of paper.

____

____

____

____

____

____

____

____

____

Lesson

78 Using a Dictionary

Guide words show the first and last entry on the page.

puma 1186 **pungency**

pu•ma ['pjumə] *n.* cougar. ⟨< Sp. < Quechua⟩

pum•ice ['pʌmɪs] *n., v.* **-iced, -ic•ing.** —*n.* Often, **pumice stone,** a light, spongy stone thrown up from volcanoes, used for cleaning, smoothing, and polishing.
—*v.* clean, smooth, or polish with pumice. ⟨ME < OF < L *pumex, -micis.* Doublet of POUNCE[2].⟩
☛ *Hom.* POMACE.

pum•mel ['pʌməl] *v.* **-melled** or **-meled, -mell•ing** or **-mel•ing.** beat; beat with the fists. Also, **pommel.**
☛ *Hom.* POMMEL ['pʌməl].

pump[1] [pʌmp] *n., v.* —*n.* **1** an apparatus or machine for forcing liquids or gases into or out of things. **2** *Informal.* the heart.
—*v.* **1** move (liquids, air, etc.) by a pump. **2** force air into by blowing or suctioning. **3** remove water, etc. (from) with a pump. **4** work a pump. **5** work as a pump does. **6** move up and down like a pump handle. **7** apply force (to) with an up and down motion. **8** *Physics.* inject or transfer energy into. **9** draw, force, supply, etc., as if by a pump. **10** *Informal.* get information out of; try to get information out of: *Don't let him pump you.*
pump iron, *Informal.* lift weights; do weightlifting exercises.
pump up, a inflate. **b** increase or strengthen; intensify; put more effort into. *The party decided that it needed to pump up its campaign.* **c** rouse to enthusiasm: *to pump up a team.* ⟨< F *pompe,* ? < Gmc.⟩ —**'pump•er,** *n.*

pump[2] [pʌmp] *n.* a low-cut shoe with no laces, straps, or other fastenings. See SHOE for picture. ⟨origin uncertain⟩

pumped [pʌmpt] *adj., v.* —*adj. Informal.* excited; enthusiastic.
—*v.* pt. and pp. of PUMP[1].

pump•er ['pʌmpər] *n.* a firetruck equipped with hoses and a water tank to pump water at the site of a fire.

pum•per•nick•el ['pʌmpər,nɪkəl] *n.* a heavy, dark, slightly sour bread made from unsifted rye flour. ⟨< G⟩

pump•kin ['pʌmpkɪn] *n.* **1** the edible fruit of any of certain trailing varieties of two plants (*Cucurbita pepo* and *C. moschata*) of the gourd family, usually very large and round or oblong in shape, with a smooth, orange or yellowish rind and golden flesh that is used as a vegetable and for pies, etc. **2** a vine that produces such fruits. ⟨alteration (with substitution of *-kin*) of earlier *pumpion* < MF *pompon* < L < Gk. *pepōn*⟩

Shows how words can be divided into **syllables**.

The most commonly used **definition** is given first. Sometimes a definition is followed by a sentence showing a use of the entry word.

Shows how the word is **pronounced**. **Accent marks** (') show which syllables receive stress. A pronunciation key may be included on each page or at the front and/or back of the dictionary.

Lists **variant** and **irregular principal parts** of verbs, and irregular forms of nouns, adjectives, and adverbs.

Tells the **part of speech**, using the abbreviations shown below.

n.	noun
pron.	pronoun
v.	verb
adj.	adjective
adv.	adverb
prep.	preposition
conj.	conjunction
interj.	interjection

Some dictionaries also include **etymologies** that show the origin and development of the word.

A. Use the dictionary entries above to answer the questions.

1. What would the last word on this page be? ______________________________
2. What are two informal meanings of pump? ______________________________
3. What word comes from an Quechuan (Incan) word? ______________________________
4. What is an informal idiom using the word pump? ______________________________
5. Which word has a homograph? ______________________________
6. Which word is a German word? ______________________________
7. What part of speech is the word pumper? ______________________________
8. What is an alternate spelling for pummel? ______________________________
9. Which word comes from a Greek word? ______________________________
10. What is a homonym of pumice? ______________________________

B. Use the pronunciation key to help you choose the correct word for each spelling given in parentheses. Underline the correct word.

1.	(grævəl)	grateful	grovel	gravel
2.	(dɔr)	dire	door	dour
3.	(rəit)	right	rate	wrote
4.	(reit)	rate	write	read
5.	(kʊd)	could	cod	kid
6.	(tʃaʊ)	chow	chew	shoe
7.	(θrɛd)	third	shred	thread
8.	(ðiz)	thighs	these	this
9.	(ʃuz)	fuzz	sues	shoes
10.	(jɜrn)	churn	yearn	cheering

[m**i**] me; [p**i**rs] p*i*erce
[**ɪ**t] *i*t

[**ei**p] *a*pe
[**ɛ**nd] *e*nd

[k**ɑ**rt] c*a*rt

[**ʌ**p] *u*p
[**əi**s] *i*ce; [w**əi**t] (wh*i*te)
[**ʌ**ut] *ou*t

[**ə**ˈbʌv] *a*bove
[t**ɜ**rn] t*u*rn
[h**ɒ**t] h*o*t; [s**ɒ**ŋ] s*o*ng

[f**ɔ**rk] (f*o*rk)
[**ɔɪ**l] (*oi*l)
[**ou**ld] (*o*ld)

[p**ʊ**l] (p*u*ll)
[r**u**l] (r*u*le)

[**θ**ɪn] (*th*in)
[**ð**ɪs] (*th*is)

[**tʃ**ɪn] (*ch*in)
[**ʃ**ɒp] (*sh*op)

[ˈtrɛ**ʒ**ər] (trea*s*ure)

[**j**uz] (*u*se)

The symbol **ə** stands for the unstressed vowel sound in **a**bout, tak**e**n, penc**i**l, lem**o**n, and circ**u**s

C. Use a dictionary to write the most common meaning of the following words. Record the page number where you found the word.

1. ingot ______________________________

2. egregious ______________________________

3. missive ______________________________

4. penchant ______________________________

5. fortuitous ______________________________

6. febrile ______________________________

7. morose ______________________________

8. dexterity ______________________________

9. binary ______________________________

10. jambalaya ______________________________

11. grandiose ______________________________

12. lacerate ______________________________

13. newspeak ______________________________

14. peptic ______________________________

15. robust ______________________________

16. secrete ______________________________

17. tenure ______________________________

18. trenchant ______________________________

Lesson 79

Using a Thesaurus

- A **thesaurus** is a reference book that writers use to find more precise or alternative words. A thesaurus lists words in alphabetical order, and each entry has a list of **synonyms**. You many find a thesaurus that provides synonyms for using a word as a noun, verb, adjective, or adverb. You may also find one that provides **antonyms**, or words that have opposite meanings. Many word-processing programs contain a thesaurus.
- When using a word from a thesaurus that you are not familiar with, check it in a dictionary first. Not all synonyms listed are interchangeable in every context.

  EXAMPLE: synonyms for the verb fear listed in a thesaurus would include "dread" and "revere," but neither would be an appropriate synonym in the following sentence: "Hugh greatly feared the dog that growled behind the fence."

Use a thesaurus to find two synonyms for each of the following words. Then use each synonym in a sentence.

fall (v.) 1. ______ 2. ______

______

______

precious (adj.) 1. ______ 2. ______

______

______

report (n.) 1. ______ 2. ______

______

______

confront (v.) 1. ______ 2. ______

______

______

slowly (adv.) 1. ______ 2. ______

______

______

build (v.) 1. ______ 2. ______

______

______

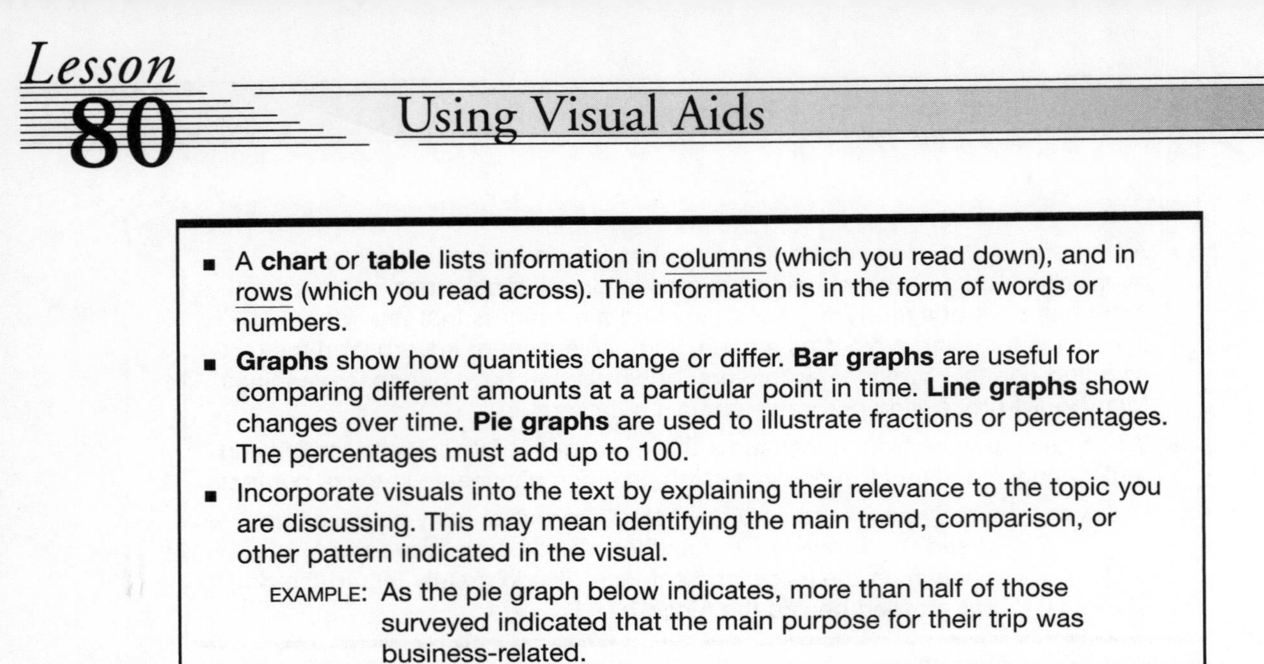

Lesson 80 Using Visual Aids

- A **chart** or **table** lists information in columns (which you read down), and in rows (which you read across). The information is in the form of words or numbers.
- **Graphs** show how quantities change or differ. **Bar graphs** are useful for comparing different amounts at a particular point in time. **Line graphs** show changes over time. **Pie graphs** are used to illustrate fractions or percentages. The percentages must add up to 100.
- Incorporate visuals into the text by explaining their relevance to the topic you are discussing. This may mean identifying the main trend, comparison, or other pattern indicated in the visual.

  EXAMPLE: As the pie graph below indicates, more than half of those surveyed indicated that the main purpose for their trip was business-related.

A. Use the chart that follows to answer the questions that appear below it.

Average hours per week of television viewing for 2- to 17-year-olds, by province, 1999

	2- to 11-year-olds	12- to 17-year-olds
	hours per week	
Newfoundland	19.0	16.3
PEI	15.9	13.0
Nova Scotia	15.3	16.8
New Brunswick	17.0	17.5
Québec	19.0	16.7
Ontario	14.9	15.3
Manitoba	15.1	14.2
Saskatchewan	16.1	15.5
Alberta	13.7	15.0
British Columbia	13.1	14.5
Canada	15.5	15.5

(Source: Statistics Canada, Catalogue no. 87F0006X1B [accessed on statcan Web site, Canadian Statistics,Culture and Leisure])

1. Which province(s) had the highest rate of TV viewing for 2- to 11-year-olds?

____

2. Which provinces have lower rates of TV viewing for 12- to 17-year-olds than for the country as a whole?

____

3. What is the rate of TV viewing for 12- to 17-year-olds in Manitoba?

____

4. Which provinces have a higher rate of TV viewing for the older group than for the younger group?

____

5. Which province has the largest difference in viewing habits between the two age groups?

____

B. **Construct a bar graph in the space below using the provincial information contained in the chart in part B on the previous page. Do not include the data for "Canada" in your graph.**

C. **Write a sentence summarizing the comparison being made in the bar graph that follows.**

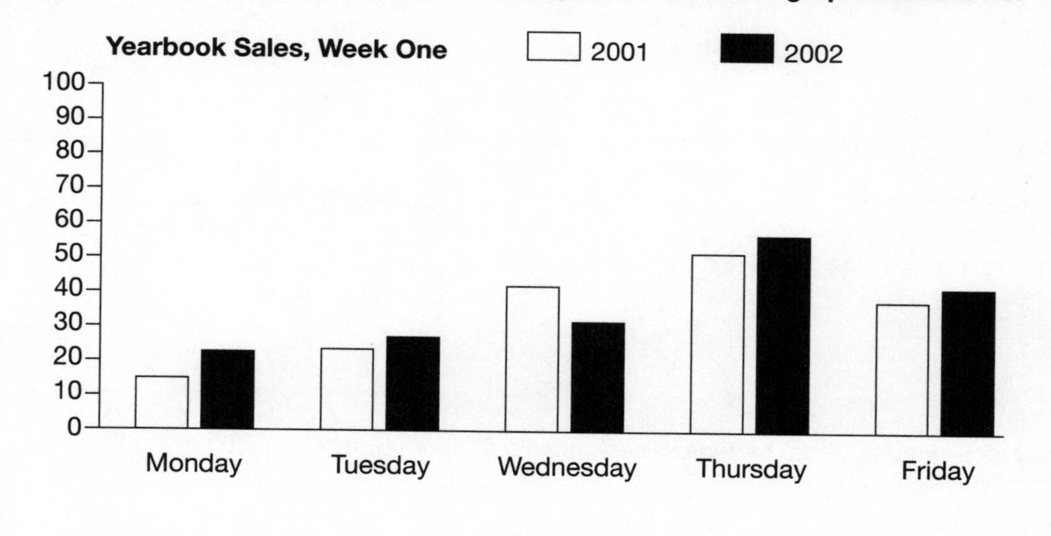

Lesson 81 Using the Library

- Books are arranged on library shelves according to **call numbers**. Each book is assigned a number from 000 to 999, according to its subject matter. The following are the main subject groups for call numbers:

000–099	Reference	500–599	Science and Mathematics
100–199	Philosophy	600–699	Technology
200–299	Religion	700–799	The Arts
300–399	Social Science	800–899	Literature
400–499	Languages	900–999	History and Geography

- In addition to books, libraries often have other resources available, including newspapers and periodicals; a vertical file containing articles, pictures, and news clippings about particular topics; an information file that includes pamphlets and information from organizations and local groups; and audiovisual materials, such as videos, films, CD's, cassettes, and DVD's.

Visit your local library or your school library and answer the following questions.

Name of Library: ______________________________

1. Where is the reference section of your library? ______________________________

2. Where is the fiction section? ______________________________

3. Where is the main library catalogue? ______________________________

4. List three magazines available at the library. Find out from the librarian how long these magazines are kept.

____

____

5. Does your library have a vertical file? ______________________________

If so, where is it kept? ______________________________

List three topics in the file. ______________________________

____

____

6. What types of audiovisual materials are available at your library? ______________________________

____

7. Are any computer databases in your library available to the public? ______________________________

If so, list two of them. ______________________________

Lesson 82 Choosing Reference Materials

- Use a **dictionary** to find the definitions and pronunciations of words and terms. Your library may contain specialized dictionaries of music, literary terms, technology, and many others.
- Use a **thesaurus** to find synonyms and antonyms.
- Use an **encyclopedia** to find basic information about many different people, places, and other subjects. An encyclopedia may also include references to related subjects.
- Use an **atlas** to find maps and information about geographical locations. Atlases may contain information about major exports, population, health, and other facts about regions and locations.
- Use an **almanac** for basic facts and statistics about history, geography, culture, and government.
- Use **periodicals** (magazines and newspapers) for information that is too current to be found in books.
- Use the **World Wide Web** for very current information, local information, or official documents that may not be available from other reference sources.

A. Indicate which of the reference sources listed above would be most likely to contain the following information.

1. the total population of China ______
2. current information about a local company ______
3. an article about Aboriginal rights ______
4. a definition of the word arpeggio ______
5. which areas in Canada are most densely populated ______
6. basic information about the life of Samuel de Champlain ______
7. a copy of the North American Free Trade Agreement ______
8. a synonym for reasonable ______
9. what Canada's borders looked like in 1866 ______
10. information about a major event in Canadian politics this week ______

- Some libraries have computers available for public use with databases on CD-ROM disks to help you locate information. **CD-ROM databases** gather a great deal of current information in a particular subject area (such as health or current affairs) from a variety of sources.
- Often, the database will include the articles and information cited. In other cases, the database provides the name of a reference source that you can look up yourself.

B. Find out what databases are available at your local library. Write the name of each database and what it contains.

____

____

____

____

- A **primary resource** is an interview, document, quotation, or account that is contemporary to your subject. For a history paper, examples include diaries, letters, and historical documents. For a scientific paper, primary resources include experiments, surveys, or other research performed by the person writing the paper.
- A **secondary resource** is a book, article, or other material that provides information about primary sources or events. For a history paper, examples include contemporary books written about what happened in the past, and opinions of notable historians. For a scientific report, secondary resources include surveys, and experiments and data collected by other researchers.

C. Following is a list of resources that you might consult for an essay comparing the childhood experiences of nineteenth-century British author Charles Dickens with those of the main character in his book *Great Expectations*. Write P next to each primary resource and S next to the secondary resources.

1. Charles Dickens' diaries ____________
2. *A Critical Study of Charles Dickens' Novels* ____________
3. *Great Expectations* by Charles Dickens ____________
4. Charles Dickens' personal letters ____________
5. A book about life in nineteenth-century London ____________

D. Use your library catalogue, the Internet, and your knowledge of Canadian history to list one primary resource and three secondary resources you might use if you were writing a paper about Canada's Constitution.

Primary Resource:

1. ____

Secondary Resources:

2. ____
3. ____
4. ____

Using the World Wide Web

- The **World Wide Web** is an international computer network that contains an overwhelming amount of data. Search engines such as Yahoo and Lycos organize information and allow users to move from site to site using a system of hypertext links.
- Although the Web is a popular up-to-date research tool, the volume of information can be frustrating. Therefore, it is important to be focussed and specific when choosing a key word to begin a search.

  EXAMPLES: Entering the key word recipes may yield thousands of hits.
  Entering the key word bread recipes narrows the search.
- Information on the Web is generally less reliable than information published in books and magazines. Web sites that are posted by governments or established organizations tend to be more reliable than those posted by individuals.

Follow the instructions below to assess sources of information on the World Wide Web.

1. Choose a topic approved by your teacher. ______________________________

   What search engine did you access? ______________________________

   What key word(s) did you use? ______________________________

2. How many sites did your key word(s) find? ______________________________

   Do any of these sources look relevant to your topic? ______________________________

   If not, narrow your search by adding to or changing your key word(s).

3. Choose the Web site that seems the most useful for your purpose and write a brief summary of its relevant content. Record the name (and e-mail address) of the author or Webmaster, the Web-site address, and the date the site was last updated.

   ____

   ____

   ____

   ____

4. Does the site provide links to other useful information? List any relevant links.

   ____

   ____

   ____

5. Would you recommend this site to other students interested in this topic? Why or why not?

   ____

   ____

Lesson 84 Acknowledging Reference Sources

- When you use another person's ideas in an essay, you must give them credit. Failure to do so is called **plagiarism**.
- There are many formats for showing the sources you use in a **Works Cited** page or **Bibliography**. Two popular formats are the Modern Languages Association (MLA) style and the American Psychological Association (APA) style. Your teacher may have a particular preference. If not, consult a style guide.

A. Arrange the following entries into a Works Cited page, following the format for entries provided by your teacher.

W. P. Kinsella. "The Kowloon Café" in Japanese Baseball and Other Stories (pages 11–35). Thistledown Press, Saskatoon. 2000.

James Sydney and Sarah Stewart. Images of Our Inheritance: A Journey Through Canada's Fragile Landscape. 1999. Whitecap Books. Vancouver.

"Caribou Shuffle," by Candace Savage. Canadian Geographic, pages 28–36. May–June 2001. Vol. 121, No. 3.

"Briton, 54, Rows Solo Across Pacific." The Toronto Star, p. A20. Saturday, March 31, 2001.

The Canadian Encyclopedia, World Edition. 1996. On CD-ROM. Toronto. McClelland & Stewart.

Dave Thompson. Alternative Rock. San Francisco. 2000. Miller Freeman Press.

Works Cited

- You should also acknowledge your sources in the body of your essay. Two ways to do this are **in-text citations** and **footnotes**. Follow the format suggested by your teacher, or consult a style guide.
- **In-text citations** include enough information (usually the author's last name, or the title of the work if there is no author) for the reader to locate the source in the Works Cited list. If appropriate, it also includes a page number to help the reader locate the exact location of the quotation or other reference.

  EXAMPLE: According to one source, "Over the past three decades, average spring temperatures in the northern Yukon have increased by an incredible six Celsius degrees" (Savage 34).
- If some of the information has been included in the body of the text, you do not have to repeat it in the in-text reference.

  EXAMPLE: Candace Savage reports that "Over the past three decades, average spring temperatures in the northern Yukon have increased by an incredible six Celsius degrees" (34).

B. Finish the following sentences by adding correct punctuation and, where necessary, a citation in parentheses in the style recommended by your teacher.

1. **From page 21 of "The Kowloon Café" (for full reference, see part A):**

   Kinsella does not explain the narrator's relationship to the café or its owner until more than halfway through the story: "I first met Charlie Wah when he came to our corporate offices to discuss our purchasing his three lots and the Kowloon Café building. I knew who he was because I had been a customer of the Kowloon Café for most of my life ____________________

2. **From page 15 of <u>Images of Our Inheritance</u> (for full reference, see part A):**

   On page 15 of <u>Images of Our Inheritance</u>, James Sydney and Sarah Stewart describe wetlands as "[a]reas where the water table meets the surface of the earth and is saturated long enough for aquatic-like processes to take place, but are too shallow to be considered a lake or pond

   ____

3. **From page 135 of <u>Images of Our Inheritance</u>:**

   Close-up encounters with whales are not always as romantic as they sound: "Perhaps the best way to describe whale breath is a literal one: it is the smell of two tonnes of partly digested fish

   ____

- If you are using **footnotes**, put a small superscript number at the end of the material you wish to credit. At the bottom of the page, put the same number, followed by the citation.

  EXAMPLE: According to one source, "Over the past three decades, average spring temperatures in the northern Yukon have increased by an incredible six Celsius degrees."[1]

  [1] Candace Savage, "Caribou Shuffle," <u>Canadian Geographic</u> May–June 2001: 34.
- The first footnote citation for a particular work should include complete bibliographic information. Subsequent references to the same work need only include the author's last name and the page number.

  EXAMPLE: [2] Savage 36.

C. Write a first-reference footnote citation in your notebook for each of the works listed in part A. Follow the format assigned by your teacher.

Review

A. Use a dictionary to answer the questions that follow.

1. Write the pronunciation for measure. ______
2. Write the most common definition of gazette. ______
3. Write the irregular forms of skid. ______
4. How many homographs are listed for the word bore? ______
5. What is the etymology of the word skate (meaning a boot with a metal blade)? ______
6. What parts of speech does the word piping function as? ______
7. Is the expression pipe down considered slang or informal? ______

B. Use a thesaurus to answer the questions that follow.

1. Find three synonyms for party (meaning a form of entertainment). Write a sentence to illustrate the meaning of each synonym.

   ______

   ______

   ______

   ______

   ______

   ______

2. List an antonym for cheerful. ______

C. Give a specific example to show how you have used (or might use) each of the following reference sources. The first one is done for you.

1. dictionary (to find the pronunciation of the word chaos)
2. thesaurus ______
3. atlas ______
4. encyclopedia ______
5. periodicals ______
6. World Wide Web ______
7. almanac ______

D. Use the chart below to answer the questions that follow.

Exercise Frequency of Canadians, 12 years and up

Age Group	Total (%)	Three or more times weekly (%)	Once or twice weekly (%)	Less than once a week or never (%)	Frequency unknown (%)
12–14 years	100.0	64.9	15.5	4.9	14.7
15–19 years	100.0	67.2	16.2	13.2	3.4
20–24 years	100.0	67.0	17.5	13.7	1.8
25–34 years	100.0	60.4	21.2	17.0	1.4
35–44 years	100.0	59.9	19.0	19.3	1.8
45–54 years	100.0	61.1	18.1	18.5	2.3
55–64 years	100.0	59.8	17.7	20.4	2.1
65 years and over	100.0	52.1	11.7	30.1	6.1

(Source: Statistics Canada, Catalogue no 82M0009XCB)

1. Which age group was least likely to exercise three or more times a week? ____________________

2. How often did most people 15 to 19 years of age exercise? ____________________

3. Which group was least likely to exercise less than once a week? ____________________

4. If you were going to translate this information into a graph, what kind of graph would be most appropriate?

____

Why? ____________________

5. Write a sentence to introduce the chart. Ensure your sentence summarizes an important pattern or trend in the chart. ____________________

____

____

E. Using resources available in your classroom, library, or at home, write entries for a Works Cited page using the format preferred by your teacher. Include the resources that follow.

1. A book ____________________

____

2. A short story in a collection ____________________

____

3. An article in an on-line magazine or newspaper ____________________

____

4. An article in a print magazine or newspaper ____________________

____

Using What You've Learned

A. Other than finding the meaning of a word, list six reasons to use a dictionary.

1. ______________________________

2. ______________________________

3. ______________________________

4. ______________________________

5. ______________________________

6. ______________________________

B. Choose the most suitable visual format for each of the following.

1. A comparison of the crime rate in all ten provinces at the end of 2001.

   ____

2. A look at the crime rate for Canada as a whole from 1965 to 2001.

   ____

3. An analysis of crimes committed in Canada in a single year, broken down by percentages into different types of crime (e.g., property crimes, violent crimes).

   ____

4. A look at how the difference between male and female crime rates has narrowed over a twenty-year period.

   ____

5. An illustration of what proportion of convictions result in a jail sentence, as compared to other outcomes, such as fines, conditional release, probation, and so on.

   ____

C. Write the call-number group in which you would find each book.

1. *World Religions* ______________________________

2. *An Introduction to Psychology* ______________________________

3. *Sculptures of Ancient Greece* ______________________________

4. *The Great Depression: 1929–1933* ______________________________

5. *A Dictionary of Musical Terms* ______________________________

6. *Algebra for Dummies* ______________________________

7. *The Story of English* ______________________________

8. *Light Metal Construction Techniques* ______

9. *The Great Thinkers* ______

10. *The Poetry of Raymond Souster* ______

D. Follow the directions below to find information for a report on a topic of your choice.

Topic: ______

1. Find three sources that relate to your topic and write a Works Cited entry for each. Try to use a variety of sources (e.g., an encyclopedia entry, a Web site, a reference book, a newspaper or magazine article).

2. What library call numbers would most likely contain information related to your topic?

3. Summarize the most important information you learned about your topic from these sources.

4. Find two other Web sites that relate to your topic. Which of the three Web sites is the most reliable? Which is the least reliable? Explain your answer.

Word Origins ■ **Write the Greek or Latin word that is included in each of the following words. Then tell what the root word means.**

	English Word	Latin or Greek Word	Meaning
1.	thermos	____________	____________
2.	ecosphere	____________	____________
3.	telemarketing	____________	____________
4.	hydroponic	____________	____________
5.	edict	____________	____________
6.	conscript	____________	____________
7.	radial	____________	____________
8.	submit	____________	____________
9.	contradict	____________	____________
10.	collaborate	____________	____________

Prefixes ■ **Add in-, im-, il-, ir-, or un- before the following words, to make new words.**

1. _______ trustworthy
2. _______ attentive
3. _______ measurable
4. _______ perfect
5. _______ reverence
6. _______ legitimate

Suffixes ■ **Add three different suffixes to each word that follows, to make new words. Watch for spelling changes.**

1. change ____________ ____________ ____________
2. happy ____________ ____________ ____________
3. convert ____________ ____________ ____________
4. supervise ____________ ____________ ____________

Idioms, Colloquialisms, and Slang ■ **Provide a more formal word or expression to replace the colloquial and slang idioms underlined in the following sentences.**

1. We were just hanging out in the park. ______________________________
2. We chewed the fat for hours. ______________________________
3. Let's take five everybody. ______________________________
4. I'm not sure that the boss has all his marbles. ______________________________
5. If you want to save your skin, you won't say that too loudly. ______________________________
6. If he beats me in the race tomorrow, I'll be eating crow! ______________________________

Denotation and Connotation ■ **For each word below, provide a synonym that has a more positive connotation.**

1. small ______________________________
2. unpredictable ______________________________
3. mob (noun) ______________________________
4. weed (noun) ______________________________
5. weak ______________________________
6. shy ______________________________
7. aggressive ______________________________

Figurative Language ■ **Underline the example of figurative language in each of the following sentences. Then write S for simile, M for metaphor, or P for personification.**

1. The cobwebs in the corner of my room waved at me languidly. ______
2. The lion made a sound like a boat engine that won't start. ______
3. She looked bleary-eyed, as if she had stayed up all night. ______
4. My legs were jelly as I climbed the stairs to the podium. ______
5. My mother is slow to anger, but when it's called for, she can be a real tiger! ______
6. The weekend awaits me, with its arms wide open! ______
7. Joy wrestled with her homework for several hours before giving up. ______
8. After her illness, Zeta had about as much energy as a wet dishrag. ______
9. After the party, the room looked like a cyclone had hit it. ______
10. When I looked down at the page, the numbers looked back at me impassively. ______

Sentence Elements ■ Underline the word or words that fit the description in parentheses.

1. (simple subject) Carmen's favourite film star will be visiting our city next month.
2. (simple predicate) I tripped over a crack while running to catch the bus.
3. (direct object) Marcel promised me a ride on his dirt bike next summer.
4. (subject complement) Those flowers smell lovely, but whenever I smell them I sneeze.
5. (indirect object) Janice handed me a fly swatter to kill the pesky fly.
6. (compound predicate) Zora and Michelle have both passed their bronze medallion exam and can now get summer jobs as lifeguards.
7. (complete subject) Paco and his brother played nearly the whole game and got three goals each.
8. (restrictive clause) Didn't the class that planted the butterfly garden do us all a great service?
9. (subordinate clause) The horse with the white patch is the one that I want to ride in the jumping competition.
10. (independent clause) When I heard what had happened, I laughed until my sides hurt!

Natural Order and Inverted Order ■ Write one sentence in natural order, and one sentence in inverted order.

1. Natural order: ____

____

2. Inverted order: ____

____

Adjective, Adverb, and Noun Clauses ■ Indicate whether the clause that is underlined is acting as a noun, adjective, or adverb clause.

1. <u>What I like best on my pancakes</u> is butter, syrup, and blueberries. ____________________
2. <u>When you turned around</u>, you accidentally hit me in the nose. ____________________
3. The Halifax explosion occurred <u>when two ships carrying explosives collided in Halifax Harbour</u>.

____

4. The card <u>that you sent</u> never arrived. ____________________
5. My coin collection is <u>what I care about most in this world</u>. ____________________

Sentence Structure ■ Write Simple, Compound, Complex, or Compound–Complex to identify the structure of the following sentences.

1. When I read that detective story, I got very involved in the plot, and I couldn't put it down until it was finished. ____________
2. Enjoy your ride in the balloon, but be careful not to lean over too far. ____________
3. If you like this band, I could get two tickets to the concert, and maybe we could go together. ____________
4. While feeling about blindly for the alarm clock, my sister upset a bowl of cereal that I had placed on her bedside table. ____________
5. To increase your grades, you have to work hard and meet your deadlines. ____________

Restrictive and Non-restrictive Elements ■ Underline the restrictive or non-restrictive element in each sentence. Add commas where necessary.

1. That chair which my grandmother gave me is about 100 years old.
2. I gave her the card that has my phone and fax numbers on it.
3. My best friend Yumiko is coming over from Japan.
4. Her mother Mrs. Fujiyama will be accompanying her.
5. The coffee table with the marble top is an antique.

Errors in Sentence Structure ■ Identify the error in the following sentences. Write P for errors in parallel structure, F for sentence fragments, RO for run-on sentences, and CS for comma splices. Then write a corrected version of the sentence.

1. ____ I will order a hot dog, a pop, and I'd like a dessert too.

   ____

2. ____ These hot dogs are delicious, where can I buy them?

   ____

3. ____ I don't know why don't you ask the vendor.

   ____

4. ____ I will go downstairs, I will get on my shoes, I will do some stretches, and then run for 40 minutes.

   ____

5. ____ A sigh of pure relief, accompanied by tears of joy, and then a feeling of deep calmness.

Grammar and Usage ▪ Read the paragraphs below and underline all the nouns. Then answer the questions that follow.

The calendar that we use today may seem like a fixed point in an ever-changing world, but in fact, it is the result of tweaking and fine-tuning over many centuries. Perhaps the most significant calendar revision was the one decreed by Julius Caesar in 46 B.C.E. Caesar simply extended that year to somewhere between 443 and 445 days. Future years, he declared, would be 365 days long, with one extra day to be added every four years, in February. This was not quite right, as it turned out, and over time the seasons had shifted so much that summer was starting in October.

Pope Gregory XIII tried to correct the problems created by the Julian calendar (named after Julius Caesar). The month of October in 1582 was shortened by 10 days. In addition, Pope Gregory adjusted the leap year by decreeing that years that ended in 00 could only be leap years if they were equally divisible by 400. It was a little complicated, but it worked. We have been using this method ever since, and summer has never once begun in October.

1. Find two verbs in a progressive tense. ______
2. Find one verb in a perfect tense. ______
3. Find one verb in the present tense. ______
4. Why is the present tense appropriate in this case? ______
5. Find one sentence in the passive voice. ______
6. Find an infinitive phrase. ______
7. Find five -ing verb forms and tell whether each is functioning as a present participle, a gerund, or a verb.

______

______

8. Find one example of a relative pronoun introducing a relative clause. ______
9. Find two examples of prepositional phrases. ______
10. Find one example of the superlative form of an adjective. ______

Subject–Verb Agreement ▪ Choose the correct verb shown in parentheses and write it in the space provided.

1. Carlos and his girlfriend, Linda, (was, were) ______ at the movie with me.
2. The team (is, are) ______ playing well these days.
3. Each of the players (has, have) ______ given up a lot for the team.
4. Either those ants or this picnic basket (is, are) ______ going to have to go.
5. There (is, are) ______ an assortment of cookies in that tin.
6. My brother or possibly my two sisters (has, have) ______ promised to help me move.

Pronoun–Antecedent Agreement ■ **Underline the antecedent and write the correct form of the pronoun in the space provided.**

1. Neither of the two girls will admit that (she, they) ______________ is wrong.
2. People in the North have (his or her, their) ______________ own perspective on life.
3. Everyone I met up there said that (he or she, they) ______________ would never leave.
4. If anybody knows (he or she, they) ______________ can't come, please let me know.
5. All of the players managed to put the loss behind (him or her, them) ______________.

Phrases ■ **Tell whether the underlined words are an infinitive, participial, gerund, or prepositional phrase.**

1. The teacher told me to edit my work more carefully. ______________
2. Wendell and I went to the hockey game last night. ______________
3. Panting and stumbling from heat and fatigue, the final marathon runner entered the stadium.
____
4. Watching the film on the big screen was very enjoyable. ______________

Double Negatives, Misplaced and Dangling Modifiers ■ **Identify each error in the following sentences as a double negative (DN), misplaced modifier (MM), or dangling modifier (DM). Then write a corrected version of each sentence.**

1. I don't hardly ever eat that much chocolate at one time! ________
____
2. Running for the bus, my umbrella got tangled in my legs. ________
____
3. We hadn't scarcely started when the lights went out. ________
____
4. While milking the cow, the pigs escaped from their pen. ________
____
5. I watched the butterfly that was looking for pollen with my high-powered glasses. ________
____

Capitalization, End Punctuation, and Quotations ▪ Rewrite the following sentences, correcting any mistakes in punctuation or capitalization.

1. "My", exclaimed Julio, "What an impressive collection of old jazz records you have"!

2. "Indeed I do." Cora insisted. "Would you like to listen to one"?

3. Julio answered "perhaps later" "first, I have a surprise for you".

4. "That is a very rare album" squealed Cora! "where did you get it"?

5. "my grandfather" he whispered reverently "once played cornet in duke ellington's band".

Punctuating Titles ▪ Add underlining or quotation marks where appropriate in the following sentences.

1. This week Sunday Night magazine has a feature titled Make Hay While the Sun Shines that is all about work.
2. The poem History Lesson by Jeannette Armstrong is published in her collection of poems titled Seventh Generation.
3. They say that the Mona Lisa has an enigmatic smile, but what does the word enigmatic mean?
4. In history class we are watching the National Film Board series Canada at War; this week we will be watching Part 4: Days of Infamy.
5. John McCrae's poem In Flanders Fields was first published in the British magazine Punch.
6. The headline in the Wessex Daily Courier read as follows: Slug Found in Milk Bottle.
7. Chapter 6 of the book Carla's Secret is called The Secret Revealed.
8. My brother's name is Atticus, just like the character in the film To Kill a Mockingbird.
9. I listened to a reading of a chapter from Margaret Atwood's book Alias Grace on the radio.
10. My favourite Leonard Cohen song is Closing Time on his The Future album.

Commas, Semicolons, and Colons ■ Insert commas, semicolons, or colons where needed.

1. I opened my pack to see what supplies were left two apples and a small bag of trail mix.
2. The places we visited were Goose Tickle Newfoundland Goose Marsh Nova Scotia Lac Goose Québec Goose Point Manitoba and Goose Spit British Columbia.
3. This my dear friend is why the television won't turn on it's not plugged in.
4. Taichi who was a tough practical self-reliant guy decided to turn to the person he trusted most himself.
5. Because of my 7 15 appointment I won't be able to make it to the concert why don't you take my ticket?

Punctuating Quotations ■ Rewrite the following sentences using ellipsis points to show that the underlined words have been omitted. Insert any words that are necessary in square brackets to clarify the meaning.

1. The film is a tour de force of extraordinary power, which contains a whole range of visual experiences, from scenes of great beauty to images of total despair.

2. I have never supported, nor will I ever support, policies that place such a heavy burden on the innocent children of our great country.

Using Other Punctuation ■ Add hyphens, apostrophes, and other missing punctuation to the following sentences. Rewrite the corrected sentence.

1. Evans red striped tie and shiny black shoes made him feel self important.

2. Carolines guest list included Michael W. Peter Q. if he was in town and Maria S.

3. The pop machines broken so we cant get any colas.

4. My well liked sister Jan who seems to have a thousand friends knows the names of two thirds of the towns teenagers.

5. By the way she has a scarcely visible scar over her left eye from falling onto hard-packed ice back in 94.

Read the following report and answer the questions that follow.

One possible alternative to fossil fuels in the short term is bio-diesel. Bio-diesel is fuel derived from sunflower or soya oil, or even from recycled cooking oil. When these products are refined, they can be used directly in a regular diesel engine, producing only about half the damaging emissions of regular diesel fuel. In addition, bio-diesel is non-toxic and biodegradable. One of the problems with this alternative is that we simply do not have enough land available for growing the crops needed to produce it. Nevertheless, it would ease the transition away from fossil fuels, and take some of the pressure off our diminishing supply.

Another short-term alternative that is already used in countries such as Italy, Argentina, and Japan is natural gas. It runs much more cleanly than gas or diesel, and it is not difficult to convert existing cars so they will run on natural gas. However, natural gas is a fossil fuel, and will eventually run out. We need longer-term, viable fuels to really solve our transportation and pollution problems.

One longer-term possibility is the development of cars that run on electricity. Electric vehicles have already been produced by the major auto companies. These cars run on a battery, and are much quieter than conventional vehicles. They produce no emissions during use, which would make cities much cleaner and more pleasant to live in. However, their environmental benefits really depend on where the electricity is generated. For example, if it is generated in coal-powered plants, the emissions would actually be higher. Therefore, it is important that these electric vehicles be powered using alternative sources of electricity, such as wind or wave power. Is this feasible on a large scale? That remains to be seen.

Finally, the newest and most promising possible replacement for conventional fuels in transportation is hydrogen fuel cells. Hydrogen is most likely the fuel of the future, although it is still not generally available. A hydrogen fuel cell combines hydrogen with oxygen to produce electricity. The only emission would be harmless water vapour. Again, the environmental impact of these fuel cells will depend on the source of hydrogen. Some form of energy is needed to separate the hydrogen from the water. If wind power could be used, this method would be completely environmentally friendly, and our best hope for the future.

The hydrogen fuel cell is still in its infancy. Several major car companies are now producing cars that run on hydrogen. In addition, hydrogen fuel buses are now being used in parts of Europe and North America. Nevertheless, before this technology can become the fuel of choice, a network of refuelling stations will have to be established. This will require a great investment in the future on the part of governments.

(Source: Adapted from Oil Won't Fuel the Future: Greenpeace Briefing on Green Transport Fuels. March 2001.)

1. Suggest a possible audience and purpose for this report.

____

____

____

2. Write a thesis statement for this report.

3. Write an opening paragraph for this report. Include the thesis.

4. Write a conclusion for the report.

5. Identify the pattern of development used by the author.

6. Find four different transition words.

7. Write the topic sentence of each paragraph.

8. Identify three elements that make this writing more formal.

Using a Dictionary and Thesaurus ▪ Find three synonyms for the word aggravate. Look up each synonym in a dictionary to clarify the meaning. Demonstrate the meaning of each synonym by using it in a sentence.

1. ______________________________

____

2. ______________________________

____

3. ______________________________

____

Using Visual Aids ▪ Write a sentence to introduce the pie graph in which you point out an important pattern or trend.

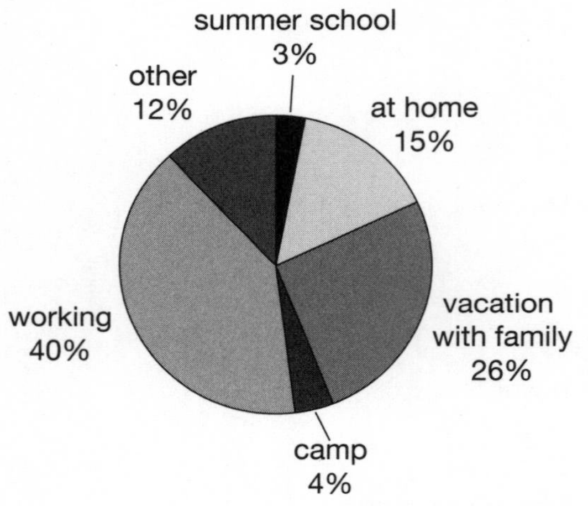

____

____

____

Using the Library ▪ Write the call number range in which each of the following titles would be found.

1. *Fine Art Masterpieces* ______________
2. *An Encyclopedia of Religion* ______________
3. *Introduction to Psychology* ______________
4. *Canadian Geography* ______________
5. *Algebra* ______________

In what part of the library, other than the stacks, would you find the following?

1. A video about endangered species ____________________
2. Newspaper clippings related to the opening of a local arts centre ____________________
3. A pamphlet describing upcoming events at the arts centre ____________________

Choosing Reference Materials ▪ Name a reference source that would be most likely to answer the following questions.

1. What is the longitude and latitude of Whitehorse, Yukon? ____________________
2. What is a synonym for rocky? ____________________
3. Where did the word hockey originate? ____________________
4. What was Madagascar's main export last year? ____________________
5. When is a new movie going to be released? ____________________

Using the World Wide Web ▪ Complete the following activities.

1. Perform a search for Web sites that contain information about karate. List the key word(s) and the search engine you used.

   ____

   ____

2. Choose two of the Web sites from the list above and record their addresses.

   ____

   ____

3. Write four facts about karate that you found on these two sites that you might use in a short paper on the subject.

   ____

   ____

   ____

   ____

Acknowledging Reference Sources ▪ Create a Works Cited or Bibliography page in your notebook using the following sources and the format recommended by your teacher.

- *The Sweet Hereafter* by Russell Banks. HarperCollins, 1991, New York.
- The short story "Aliens," by Katherine Govier. Found in the collection of her stories called *The Immaculate Conception Photography Gallery*. Published in 1994 by Little, Brown and Company in Boston.
- Article in the May–June 2001 edition of *Canadian Geographic* magazine, pages 54 to 62, titled "Power Switch," written by Lawrence Scanlan.

Index